DESIGN AND TECHNOLOGY

# *Curriculum* Bank

## KEY STAGE TWO
## SCOTTISH LEVELS C-E

# DESIGN AND TECHNOLOGY

RICHARD AGER

**Published by Scholastic Ltd,**
Villiers House,
Clarendon Avenue,
Leamington Spa,
Warwickshire CV32 5PR
Text © Richard Ager
© 1997 Scholastic Ltd
234567890 7890123456

**AUTHOR**
RICHARD AGER

**EDITOR**
LIBBY RUSSELL

**SERIES DESIGNER**
LYNNE JOESBURY

**DESIGNER**
CLAIRE BELCHER

**ILLUSTRATIONS**
THE DRAWING ROOM
AND GARRY DAVIES

**COVER ILLUSTRATION**
JONATHAN BENTLEY

**INFORMATION TECHNOLOGY CONSULTANT**
MARTIN BLOWS

**SCOTTISH 5–14 LINKS**
MARGARET SCOTT AND SUSAN GOW

Designed using Aldus Pagemaker
Printed in Great Britain by Ebenezer Baylis, Worcester

British Library Cataloguing-in-Publication Data
A catalogue record for this book is available from the
British Library.

ISBN 0-590-53405-X

# Contents

DESIGN AND TECHNOLOGY

With thanks to Ann for her encouragement and support, and to Jenny, Sarah and Siân for trying out many of the activities before they were used in schools.

# Introduction

*Scholastic Curriculum Bank* is a series for all primary teachers, providing an essential planning tool for devising comprehensive schemes of work as well as an easily accessible and varied bank of practical, classroom-tested activities with photocopiable resources.

Designed to help planning for and implementation of progression, differentiation and assessment, *Scholastic Curriculum Bank* offers a structured range of stimulating activities with clearly stated learning objectives that reflect the programmes of study, and detailed lesson plans that allow busy teachers to put ideas into practice with the minimum amount of preparation time. The photocopiable sheets that accompany many of the activities provide ways of integrating purposeful application of knowledge and skills, differentiation, assessment and record-keeping.

Opportunities for formative assessment are highlighted within the activities where appropriate, while separate summative assessment activities give guidelines for analysis and subsequent action. Ways of using information technology for different purposes and in different contexts, as a tool for communicating and handling information and as a means of investigating, are integrated into the activities where appropriate, and more explicit guidance is provided at the end of the book.

The series covers all the primary curriculum subjects, with separate books for Key Stages 1 and 2 or Scottish Levels A–B and C–E. It can be used as a flexible resource with any scheme, to fulfil National Curriculum and Scottish 5–14 requirements and to provide children with a variety of different learning experiences that will lead to effective acquisition of skills and knowledge.

**DESIGN AND TECHNOLOGY**

# INTRODUCTION

The *Scholastic Curriculum Bank Design and Technology* books enable teachers to plan comprehensive and structured coverage of the programmes of study, and pupils to develop the required skills and understanding through activities that promote design and technology capability.

There are two books for Design and Technology – one for Key Stage 1 and one for Key Stage 2. The activities in this KS2 book build upon the skills, knowledge and understanding which have been developed at Key Stage 1.

## Bank of activities

This book provides a bank of activities that can be used in many different ways to form a framework for a scheme of work. They can provide breadth, variety or extension to a core scheme; support a cross-curricular topic; or the Investigative, Disassembly and Evaluative Activities (IDEAs) and Focused Practical Tasks (FPTs) can be used separately to help to address particular learning needs.

## Range

The range of activities provided will enable children to develop both their process and practical skills, and their knowledge and understanding about materials, structures, mechanisms, control products and their application and health and safety.

## Communication skills

The activities aim to develop language and communication skills by encouraging children to:
▲ use technical vocabulary, diagrams and symbols;
▲ describe and discuss their work and respond to questioning;
▲ present their work using writing, quality products and a variety of drawing and modelling techniques.

## Lesson plans

Detailed lesson plans, under clear headings, are given for each activity and are set out in a standard way so that the material is easy to follow and can be readily implemented in the classroom. The structure for each activity is as follows.

### *Activity title box*

Each activity has been designated as either an IDEA (investigative, disassemble and evaluative activity) or as a FPT (focused practical task).

The information in the title box at the beginning of each activity outlines the following key aspects:
▲ *Activity title and learning objective* – Each activity has clearly stated learning objectives given in bold italics. These learning objectives break down aspects of the programmes of study into manageable teaching and learning units and their purpose is to aid planning for breadth and balance. These objectives can be easily referenced to the National Curriculum and Scottish 5–14 requirements by using the overview grids at the end of this chapter (pages 9 to 12).
▲ *Class organisation/Likely duration* – Icons ✝✝ and 🕒 signpost the suggested group sizes for each activity and the approximate amount of time required to complete it. Timing arrangements are, by their very nature, arbitrary, as so many factors are involved, including the children's previous skills and knowledge. However, it is important that the children are aware that there are constraints on the amount of time available, just as there are in the 'real world' of designers, manufacturers and producers.
▲ *Health and safety* – Where necessary, health and safety considerations are flagged by the icon ⚠. However it is essential that checks are made as to what LEA regulations are in place and further guidance can be obtained from the booklets *Make it Safe: Safety guidance for the teaching of Design and Technology at Key Stages 1 and 2*, National Association of Advisors and Inspectors in Design and Technology (NAAIDT) and *Be Safe* published by the Association for Science (ASE).

### *Previous skills/knowledge needed*

The information given here alerts teachers to particular knowledge or skills that the children need prior to carrying out the activity.

### *Key background information*

The information in this section is intended to set the scene and provide helpful guidance for teachers which may relate to children's learning, teachers' knowledge the subject, or both. It may go beyond the level expected of most children, but gives teacher confidence to ask and answer questions.

### *Vocabulary*

This section contains key words which should be introduced to the children at some point during the activity.

### Preparation

Advice is given for those occasions where it is necessary for the teacher to prepare the children for an activity (such as asking them to bring in a particular item from home to investigate) or to collect and prepare materials ahead of time.

### Resources needed

All the equipment, materials and photocopiable sheets needed to carry out the activity are listed here, so that the children or the teacher can gather them together easily before the beginning of the teaching session. In the designing and making assignments (DMAs) section, the resources are only *possible suggestions*, as the children must have the opportunity to make some choices for themselves.

### What to do

Easy-to-follow, step-by-step instructions are given for carrying out the activity, including, where appropriate, suggestions for suitable points for discussion. Issues of classroom management are raised where relevant.

### Suggestion(s) for extension/support

Where possible, ways of extending or modifying tasks, for easy differentiation, are suggested. Thus activities are accessible to both more and less able pupils.

### Assessment opportunities

Each investigative, disassemble and evaluative activity (IDEA) and focused practical task (FPT) has clearly staged assessment opportunities which relate directly to the learning objectives for that activity and provide the framework for ongoing assessment. By taking advantage of these assessment opportunities, teachers can be reassured that the stated learning objectives have been covered. Where appropriate, teachers' questions for eliciting information from children are also included.

### Opportunities for IT

Where opportunities for IT present themselves, these are briefly outlined with reference to particularly suitable types of program. The chart on page 158 presents specific areas of IT covered in the activities, together with more detailed support on how to apply particular types of program. Selected lesson plans serve as models for other activities by providing more comprehensive guidance on the application of IT, and these are indicated by the bold page numbers on the grid and the ⬦ icon at the start of an activity.

### Display ideas

In this section ideas for display in the classroom are incorporated into activity plans. It is important that displays are often interactive and 3-D in nature, as well as the more typical wall display.

### Reference to photocopiable sheets

Where activities include photocopiable sheets, small facsimiles of the relevant sheets are included in the lesson plans, with notes describing how they can be used to assist the teacher in planning.

## Assessment

The design and make assignments allow teachers to make summative assessments about their children's design and technology capability. Using all the evidence which is collected throughout the DMAs, such as observations, discussions, design drawings, modelling and the finished product, the children can be assessed against the level descriptors for *designing* and for *making*, deciding which level best fits or describes the work of each child.

## Photocopiable sheets

Many of the activities are accompanied by photocopiable sheets. These often lead the children carefully through particular skill-based activities. Other sheets provide background information, and some give opportunities for children to record progress they have made in their work. The latter can be used as evidence to support the assessments you make of the children.

## Cross-curriculuar links

Cross-curricular links are identified on a simple grid (see page 160) which cross-references particular areas of study in design and technology to the work which could be undertaken in other subject areas.

## DESIGN AND TECHNOLOGY

The National Curriculum states that design and technology capability can be developed through *combining designing and making skills with knowledge and understanding in order to design and make products.* It is for that reason that most of the activities in this book concentrate on designing and making, utilising new skills and knowledge which should be introduced to the children.

To develop the children's capability, the Order sets out three types of activity in which they should engage. These are investigative, disassemble and evaluative activities (IDEAs), focused practical tasks (FPTs) and design and make assignments (DMAs). However, it is worthwhile considering the close links which exist between these three types of work.

Each of the main chapters includes mainly FPTs, sometimes with a few additional IDEAs. However, good design and technology teaching will start with some scene-setting and this will almost always take the form of an IDEA. For example, the activity on tie-dying would benefit from looking at the existing tie-dye products, and getting the children to consider the ways in which the designs were achieved. The IDEAs that are given in this book can be considered as samples, providing a framework for investigation, disassembly or evaluation, which you can use to develop your own introductory sessions to many other FPTs described in these pages.

A DMA is, by its very nature, more open-ended than many other activities. It must give children the opportunity to make real choices in terms of processes, practical techniques and

the use of equipment and materials. Some constraints will be necessary to prevent the activity becoming completely unmanageable, although there must remain an opportunity for choice.

With small changes, it should be clear that many of the FPTs could easily become design and make assignments. By being less prescriptive in the way in which the material is taught, and by allowing the children to be more individually responsible for some of the decisions that have to be made, you can transform a focused activity with its introductory IDEA into a complete DMA.

The relevance of this is that it is not the actual content of the activity which determines its nature, but the way in which the learning is managed by the teacher. The only significant feature of the DMAs, that are included in their own chapter, is that they cover topics which, very obviously, involve a diverse range of materials which children can choose to work in. It should also be noted that they include lists of materials which children may wish to use – they are not meant to be exhaustive.

At Key Stage 2, children need to be given opportunities to develop their design and technology capability through:
▲ working with a range of materials which includes sheet materials, materials for making frameworks, mouldable materials, textiles, food, electrical and mechanical components and constructions kits;
▲ working independently and within teams;
▲ applying skills, knowledge and understanding from other subjects, particularly mathematics and science.

They should be taught a wide range of designing skills, including generating and communicating their ideas, planning, and evaluating and making skills including the selection of appropriate materials, tools and equipment, use of appropriate finishing techniques, evaluation of their products and the implementation of improvements which they identify.

The knowledge base at Key Stage 2 includes materials and components, control, structures, products and applications, quality, health and safety, and vocabulary. The first three areas are covered by the FPTs, and products and applications are considered in the IDEAs. The other issues are discussed throughout the book, with sections on health and safety, and vocabulary occurring in each chapter, and with the emphasis on quality being developed as a theme in all aspects of the children's practical work.

An important feature of Design and Technology is that it is so broad in nature. While an understanding of technical issues is important there are also many opportunities for children to display their artistic flair, both during the designing process and also when it comes to finishing their products.

Much evidence exists to show that children enjoy designing and making activities. This books aims to provide you with some stimulus material which will assist you in enabling children to engage in design and technological activities and give them opportunities to make their own decisions, to be creative and to solve practical problems.

| Learning objective | PoS/AO | Content | Type of activity | Page |
|---|---|---|---|---|
| **Structures** | | | | |
| *To develop their ability to make simple shell structures; developing measuring and cutting skills.* | 4c; 5a, e. *Technology: Design Process* – *Practical skills: Level C.* | Making packaging. | FPT Working individually. | 14 |
| *To investigate how paper beams can be made stronger.* | 5a, e. *Properties of materials: Level C.* | Carrying out 'fair tests' by loading beams made from paper to destruction. | IDEA Working in pairs. | 15 |
| *To develop their designing, making and planning skills in the context of building a beam bridge.* | 3b–d, f; 4a–c, e, f; 5a, e. *Design and manufacturing processes: Level D.* | Building a beam bridge from square-section wood, focusing on stability, depth of beam and rigidity. | FPT Groups of four. | 17 |
| *To develop the skills and techniques appropriate for constructing with artstraws and pipe cleaners.* | 3f; 4b, c, f; 5a, e. *Practical skills: Level D.* | Building a geodesic structure. | FPT Working in pairs. | 18 |
| *To develop skills and techniques appropriate for constructing with rolled-up paper tubes.* | 3b–d, f; 4a–c, e, f; 5a, e. *As above.* | Building an obstacle course. | FPT Working in pairs. | 20 |
| *To develop skills in accurately cutting and measuring square-section wood, planning and collaborative working.* | 3b–d, f; 4a–c, e, f; 5a, e. *As above.* | Designing and making a model Tudor House. | FPT Working in pairs. | 21 |
| **Mechanisms** | | | | |
| *To understand the importance of evaluating existing products before designing and making your own.* | 5f. *Effectiveness of design: Level D.* | Evaluating their own toys. | IDEA Working in pairs. | 24 |
| *To develop children's understanding of pneumatics. To build a simple model incorporating these ideas.* | 5c. *Science: Energy and Forces* – *Forces and their effects: Level D.* | Building a model car park barrier using square-section wood and syringes. | FPT Working in pairs. | 25 |
| *To develop children's understanding of cams. To understand the purpose and value of prototyping.* | 5c. *As above.* | Designing and making a simple toy which could be used to advertise an event, utilising cams. | FPT Working in pairs. | 27 |
| *To understand the basic features of levers.* | 5c. *As above.* | Making a model using levers to illustrate a nursery rhyme. | FPT Working individually. | 29 |
| *To understand the basic principles of gearing.* | 5c. *As above.* | Making a simple matchstick gear wheel. | FPT Groups of three. | 30 |
| *To gain an understanding of how gears can transfer motion through a right angle.* | 5c. *As above.* | Making a hand-operated zoetrope. | FPT Groups of three or four. | 31 |
| *To gain an understanding of the principles of simple pulleys.* | 5c. *As above.* | Designing and making a conveyor belt system. | FPT Groups of four. | 33 |

| Learning objective | PoS/AO | Content | Type of activity | Page |
|---|---|---|---|---|
| **Energy** | | | | |
| *To investigate the types of energy that are used in school to increase their awareness of the different kinds of energy.* | 3a. *As above.* | Produce an energy map of their own school. | IDEA Groups of four. | 36 |
| *To gain an understanding of how energy can be stored in objects and how it can be slowly released.* | 5c. *As above.* | Investigations with balloons and elastic bands. | FPT Working in pairs. | 37 |
| *To make children aware of the idea of getting energy from water and to enhance their IT skills.* | 3a. *Conversion of energy: Level D.* | Doing a presentation on water power. | IDEA Groups of five to eight. | 38 |
| *To build a simple water-wheel that will lift a load and to gain an understanding of evaluation criteria.* | 3g; 5a, c. *As above.* | Building a water-wheel. | FPT Working in pairs. | 40 |
| *To develop an awareness of how the wind provides us with energy.* | 3a. *As above.* | Focused research into wind power. | IDEA Working individually. | 41 |
| *To make use of their knowledge of wind power and pulleys, and to develop their evaluative skills.* | 3a, f, g; 4e–g; 5a–c. *Properties and uses: Level D.* | Make a vehicle that travels towards the wind. | FPT Groups of five. | 42 |
| *To overcome problems encountered during designing and making and to develop evaluative skills.* | 3a, f, g; 4e–g; 5a–c. *Transfer of energy: Level D.* | Design and make a propeller-powered boat. | FPT Working in pairs. | 44 |
| *To understand the basic principles of how a hovercraft works.* | 5a, e, g. *Forces and their effects: Level D.* | Design and make a hovercraft. | FPT Working in pairs. | 45 |
| **Mouldable materials** | | | | |
| *To develop skills and techniques related to working with papier mâché in a co-operative way.* | 2b; 5a, b. **Technology –** *Properties of materials: Level C.* | Making a pair of maracas. | FPT Working in pairs. | 48 |
| *To develop skills and techniques related to working with Formello or Fimo modelling medium.* | 4a–c; 5a, b. *As above.* | Designing and making some jewellery. | FPT Working individually. | 49 |
| *To develop skills and techniques related to working with Plastazote.* | 4a–c; 5a, b. *As above.* | Designing and making some body protection for a sporting activity. | FPT Groups of four. | 51 |
| *To develop skills and techniques related to working with clay.* | 4a–c; 5a, b. *As above.* | Making small clay pots. | FPT Working individually. | 52 |
| *To develop skills and techniques related to working with salt dough.* | 4a–c; 5a, b. *As above.* | Making articles for sale at a craft fair. | FPT Working individually. | 54 |
| *To develop skills and techniques related to working with Mod Roc.* | 4a–c; 5a, b. As above. | Designing and making masks. | FPT Groups of four. | 55 |
| **Food** | | | | |
| *To make children aware of the importance of food hygiene and safety.* | 5j. **Health Education –** *Health and safety in the environment: Level C.* | Identifying mistakes when working with food. | IDEA As a class, then individually. | 58 |

DESIGN AND
TECHNOLOGY

| Learning objective | PoS/AO | Content | Type of activity | Page |
|---|---|---|---|---|
| To teach children methods of evaluating the preferences of people for different products. | 3b; 5i, j. *Collecting evidence: Level C.* | Carrying out tasting tests on ready-made soups. | IDEA Groups of four. | 59 |
| To understand what a food label tells us. | 3a. *Interpreting: Level C.* | Researching the information on a food label. | IDEA Working in pairs. | 61 |
| To make children aware of a method of changing the texture and taste of a food product. | 4f; 5b. *Applying skills: Level C.* | Making butter from cream. | FPT Working in pairs. | 63 |
| To adapt recipes to appeal to particular people. To follow instructions/measure accurately. | 3a, b; 4e. *As above.* | Making bread rolls. | FPT Working in pairs. | 64 |
| To use their knowledge of taste and colour to develop an interesting healthy fruit drink. | 3a, b, d; 4a, e, f; 5b. *As above.* | Making a children's fruit cocktail. | FPT Groups of four. | 65 |

**Textiles**

| Learning objective | PoS/AO | Content | Type of activity | Page |
|---|---|---|---|---|
| To be aware of the characteristics of different fabrics. | 3a; 5a, b, f. **Technology –** *Selecting and using the design process: Level C.* | Investigation into the properties of different fabrics and their labels. | IDEA Working in pairs. | 68 |
| To practise a range of stitches. | 5a, b. *As above.* | Design and make a simple cross-stitch bookmark. | FPT Working individually. | 70 |
| To learn and develop the skills involved in tie-dying and to develop sewing skills. | 3a; 4d; 5b. *As above.* | To make a small bag using tie-dyed fabric. | FPT Working in pairs. | 71 |
| To learn and develop the techniques used in Batik. | 3a, b; 4d; 5b. *As above.* | To make a place mat using Batik techniques. | FPT Working individually. | 72 |
| To practise skills of sewing and using a pattern. To develop ideas through brainstorming. | 3a; 4b, c, e; 5e. *As above.* | To make a simple glove puppet of a character of their own choosing. | FPT Working in groups of four, then individually. | 74 |
| To practise skills of using a pattern and sewing. | 3a; 4b, c, e; 5e. *As above.* | To make a small stuffed toy from a given pattern. | FPT Working individually. | 75 |

**Electricity**

| Learning objective | PoS/AO | Content | Type of activity | Page |
|---|---|---|---|---|
| To disassemble torches to help find out how they work, and to draw an exploded diagram. | 3c; 5f, g. *Properties and uses of energy: Level D.* | Investigate and draw an exploded diagram of a torch. | IDEA Working individually. | 78 |
| To look carefully at a wide range of switches to find out how they can be used and to make some of their own. | 5d, f. *As above.* | An investigation of a wide range of different switches and then letting the children build some. | IDEA Groups of four, then pairs. | 79 |
| To use simple electrical switches and circuits, and introduce the technique of soldering. | 3b, e, f; 4a, c, e, g; 5d. *As above.* | Design and make a simple model incorporating LEDs and switches. | FPT Individually or in pairs. | 81 |
| To make children aware of the construction and uses of a membrane switch. | 3a; 4b, c, f; 5d. *As above.* | To design and make a membrane switch which detects a person entering the classroom. | FPT Working in pairs. | 82 |

**DESIGN AND TECHNOLOGY**

| Learning objective | PoS/AO | Content | Type of activity | Page |
|---|---|---|---|---|
| To make use of their knowledge of switches and circuits in a problem-solving context. | 3b, e, f; 4a, c, e, g; 5d. *As above.* | To design and make a burglar alarm to protect valuables within the school. | FPT Working in pairs. | 84 |
| To apply their knowledge of pulleys and motors in a new context. | 4b. *Properties and uses of energy: Level D.* | Making a motorised buggy. | FPT Working in pairs. | 86 |
| **Control** | | | | |
| To develop an existing product of their own. To explore some form of automatic control. | 5d. *Technology: Design process* – Devices and tools associated with control: Level D. | To incorporate a flashing light onto an existing buggy. | FPT Discussing as a group, making individually. | 90 |
| To learn how to use a two-way switch to reverse a motor and to incorporate it into a model. | 5d. *As above.* | To incorporate an automatic reversing switch into a small buggy. | FPT Working in pairs and then individually. | 90 |
| To understand that a computer control program is basically a series of automatic switches. | 5d. *As above.* | To write a computer program to control sets of traffic lights. | FPT Working in groups of four. | 92 |
| To develop knowledge of control using a membrane keypad followed by a computer. | 5d. *As above.* | To design and build a museum display with a range of electrical devices. | FPT Working in groups of four. | 93 |
| **Design and make assignments** | | | | |
| To design and make a photograph frame. | 3a–g; 4a–g; 5a, b, e, h, i, j. *Technology: Design process* – Selecting and using the design process: Level D. | Most likely working with wood – perhaps plastic or textiles. Possible finishing using mouldable materials. | DMA Working in pairs, then individually. | 96 |
| To design and make an electrical game for a particular market. | 3a–g; 4a–g; 5a, b, d, f–j. *As above.* | Using electrical components. Probably using sheet materials. | DMA Working in groups of four. | 98 |
| To design and make a prototype of a lamp. To identify a market for the lamp. | 3a–g; 4a–g; 5a, b, d, f–j. *As above.* | Using electrical components. Probably using square-section wood or rolled up paper tubes. | DMA Working in pairs. | 99 |
| To design and make a pair of slippers. | 3a–g; 4a–g; 5a, b, f–j. *As above.* | Probably using textiles or Plastazote, card or other sheet material. | DMA Working in pairs. | 100 |
| To design, make and evaluate a new snack for a particular market. | 3a–g; 4a–g; 5a, b, f–j. *As above.* | Using food products and graphics skills. | DMA Groups of four. | 101 |
| To choose appropriate electrical components, mechanisms and constructional materials in order to design and make a fairground ride. | 3a–g; 4a–g; 5a–d, f–j. *As above.* | Probably using square-section wood, sheet materials, electrical devices. | DMA Working in groups of four. | 102 |
| To design and make a string puppet. To identify a need for a puppet and select materials. | 3a–g; 4a–g; 5a, b, d–j. *As above.* | Probably using papier mâché, textiles and perhaps electrical components. | DMA Groups of six, then individuals. | 103 |

DESIGN AND TECHNOLOGY

# Structures

This section looks at a range of materials that can be used to build basic structures. There are two main groups known as frame structures and shell structures. The following activities show how square-section wood, rolled up paper tubes and Jumbo artstraws can be used to make frame structures, and how cardboard can be used to make shell structures.

The basic principles which these activities consider are stability, strength and triangulation. All the focused practical tasks involve the children in building structures, and they are introduced to a wide range of techniques. It is these principles of construction which will be used extensively in much of the other work which the children undertake in Design and Technology.

## FLAT PACKAGING  ◇ FPT

*To develop children's ability to make a simple shell structures and to identify uses for these packages. To give children an opportunity to develop their measuring and cutting skills.*

†† *Pairs and then individuals.*

🕐 *1 hour.*

⚠ *Make sure the children know how to score safely. If they use a craft knife ensure they have been given clear safety instructions on how to use it, and closely observe those using them.*

### Previous skills/knowledge needed

Children will need to be able to cut, score and fold. They will also have an understanding that material can be strengthened by being folded or rolled. It will be useful if they have covered work on nets in mathematics.

### Key background information

There are two basic types of structure – shell structures and frame structures. A shell structure is normally made out of flat sheet material, which is cut and folded to give it strength.

### Vocabulary

Shell, frame.

### Preparation

You will need copies of photocopiable sheets 106, 107 and 108 to give to the children. Once copied, sheet 106 should be cut in half so that half the class get one set of examples and the other children get a different set. Sheets 107 and 108 should be photocopied onto card. (Alternatively, sheets could be stuck onto card.) You also need the packages on photocopiable pages 107 and 108 made up to assist children who may be having problems (see 'Suggestion(s) for support').

### Resources needed

Corrugated cardboard, scissors, metal safety rule (optional: craft knife, rotary cutter, perforation cutter), cutting mat, solid glue stick, photocopiable sheets 106, 107 and 108.

### What to do

Remind children that material is strengthened when it is folded or curved. Give examples of the technique in action such as corrugated cardboard, corraflute and the tube inside kitchen rolls. Sheet 106 includes lots of examples of sheet material being folded and hence strengthened. Give half the class the top of sheet 106 and the other half the bottom. In pairs, ask them to think of other examples of sheet material being used in this way. Get each pair to give one suggestion and see if it is included on the other half of the sheet.

Now the children can make two simple shell structures. This activity could be used as an introduction to rotary and

perforation cutters and the safe use of craft knives, metal rulers and cutting mats, although it can be completed by using just scissors. Demonstrate the use of the rotary cutter, particularly when cutting along curved lines, and the perforation cutter – emphasise that pushing down too hard will cut through the card, rather than just score it.

Ask the children to make the shell structure on sheet 107. They should cut on the solid lines and score on the dotted lines. Use a solid glue stick to stick the edges together. Ideally, they should be encouraged to fold the nets inwards so that the lines do not show – but this is more difficult. When the ends are folded in you will have a solid shell structure. Ask the children what the structure could be used for. It is similar to the containers used in fast food restaurants for holding fruit pies. Discuss the advantages of a package which is stored flat, but which can be easily folded into a strong structure.

Children can then repeat the activity with the more complex shape on sheet 108. They can again suggest uses for the finished packaging. In this case, the package is similar to the French fries containers in fast food restaurants, but they could be used for sweets or small gifts for example.

DESIGN AND TECHNOLOGY

## Suggestion(s) for extension

Children could use the principles learned to design their own packaging from a net of their own design. This could be enhanced by having a range of cardboard packages to be disassembled by the children so that they understand the way in which they are put together.

## Suggestion(s) for support

Examples of the two packages could be made up to give children who are having difficulties some assistance.

## Assessment opportunities

This activity is ideal for assessing the accuracy of children's cutting and scoring. By careful questioning of the children it should be possible to determine their understanding that folding sheet material can produce rigid structures.

## Opportunities for IT

The children could use a drawing package to plan out the nets for their own packaging. 'Turn on' a background of grid squares set at 1cm intervals – this will help the children obtain accurate measurements for the net. If the software has a 'snap to grid' facility this will enable them to line up the sides of the cubes accurately and at 90 degrees. The completed nets can be printed out, on this card or thicker paper, and then made up.

The children could also use framework software such as My World 2 with some of the 'Design a Building' series of files which will print out the net of the designed building, complete with the flaps for gluing.

## Display ideas

The finished packages could be decorated highlighting the particular use to which they could be put. This could involve either the initial designs being put to more unusual uses or totally new designs.

## Reference to photocopiable sheets

Sheet 106 shows a range of shell structures and is cut in half for the children to use as reminders. Sheets 107 and 108 contain the nets of two packages. By making these two structures, the children experience how relatively strong structures can be made from sheet materials.

## BEAMS

**IDEA**

*To investigate how beams made from paper can be made stronger.*

†† *Working in pairs.*

⏱ *1 hour session.*

⚠ *Take care when using weights in these activities. They can cause damage if they are dropped onto the floor.*

### Previous skills/knowledge needed

Children should be familiar with 'fair tests' from their science work. In this activity they will need to ensure that their beams are always made up using the same amount of paper.

### Key background information

Beams are made stronger by being deeper. The distance between the top and bottom of a beam is more important than the material between them. If you build a beam that is very deep, there is a danger that it will become unstable and topple over. Therefore a compromise has to be made between depth and width.

### Vocabulary

Beam, compromise.

### Resources needed

Photocopiable sheet 109 per pair of children, A4 paper and card, solid glue stick, books, masses, scissors.

### What to do

Talk to the group about beams. A plank of wood is a beam – so is a metre rule. If you put a metre rule across two stools (to form a simple bridge) and press down on it, it bends very easily. If you now put the metre rule on its edge and do the same thing you will find it very difficult to bend. The same ruler, the same material, but it is able to withstand a much greater force when it is on its edge. It is this depth of the beam which is so important in providing strength.

The most common shape of beam is probably the H-beam (see Figure 1.1).

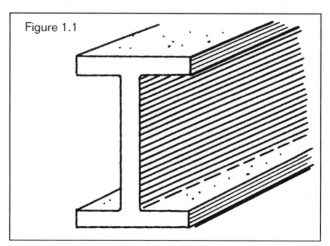

Figure 1.1

DESIGN AND
TECHNOLOGY

It is designed to be as strong as possible with the least amount of material. The flat bits at the top and bottom are there for stability – it needs a wide base so that it does not topple over and a wide top for things to travel over (in the case of a beam bridge) or for bricks to be cemented to (in the case of a beam in a house).

To make the beam strong there needs to be as much space between the top and the bottom, but there does not have to be a great thick piece of metal keeping them apart. If there was, this would just make the beam much too heavy and much too expensive. So the metal keeping the top and bottom of the beam apart is usually very thin, and it often has holes in, for example, beams in large warehouses often have this shape. You may wonder why someone has spent time cutting out all the attractive holes in the metal, but in fact the beam was manufactured to be much narrower, and is carefully cut, moved along and then welded together in the new position (see Figures 1.2 and 1.3). This creates a beam which is stronger but uses no more metal!

The important feature to get over to children is that to make a beam strong it must be deep, but while making it deep, you also have to make sure that it is still stable, by making the base quite wide.

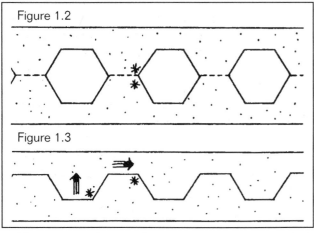

Figure 1.2

Figure 1.3

Now give each pair photocopiable sheet 109 which suggests a number of ways to fold an A4 sheet of paper so that it can take a load. Ask them to create a gap using two piles of books which has to be crossed with a bridge (see Figure 1.4).

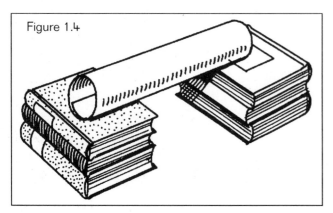

Figure 1.4

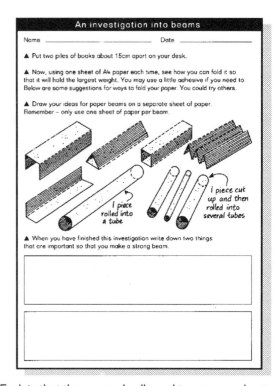

**An investigation into beams**

Name _____  Date _____

▲ Put two piles of books about 15cm apart on your desk.

▲ Now, using one sheet of A4 paper each time, see how you can fold it so that it will hold the largest weight. You may use a little adhesive if you need to. Below are some suggestions for ways to fold your paper. You could try others.

▲ Draw your ideas for paper beams on a separate sheet of paper. Remember – only use one sheet of paper per beam.

1 piece rolled into a tube

1 piece cut up and then rolled into several tubes

▲ When you have finished this investigation write down two things that are important so that you make a strong beam.

Explain that they are only allowed to use one sheet of A4 paper, rather than metal, to make the bridges, but they should think about the principles discussed at the start of the lesson. Can they make it strong enough to hold the masses? At the end of the session, each pair should choose two features which they think are important about the strongest beams they have built. Their comments will probably relate to the strength of a bridge with corrugations or where the paper is rolled up. Their findings can be related back to the idea that sheet materials can be given rigidity when they are folded.

### Suggestion(s) for extension
Ask the children to look for beams in buildings, and to draw them. They should annotate these drawings pointing out their significant features in terms of depth, stability and triangulation. Ask the children how the design of shelves has to take into account the work they have done on beams – a deeper shelf can take a greater load, as can a thicker shelf; brackets have to be closer together as the load increases.

### Suggestion(s) for support
Pairs can be carefully chosen for this activity so that they contain a mix of abilities.

### Assessment opportunities
This activity gives opportunities to identify how well children can relate the theoretical background of their work to real life situations.

### Opportunities for IT
The children could use a drawing package to draw a picture of their strongest beam and add text about the factors which made it strong.

### Display ideas

Ask each pair to draw a picture of their strongest beam, and write down the two factors which they think make it strongest. Make a wall display of the children's drawings and bring out the common factors in big lettering at the top of the display.

### Reference to photocopiable sheet

Sheet 109 shows the possible beam shapes which need to be investigated. The children record their paper beam ideas and write down the reasons why some shapes are stronger than others.

## BEAM BRIDGE   ◇ FPT

*To develop designing and making skills, utilising specific areas of knowledge, such as structures.*
*To develop their planning skills.*

†† *Working in groups of four.*
🕐 *Three one-hour sessions.*
⚠ *Children should know how to use a saw safely.*

### Previous skills/knowledge needed

General information on bridges. Children already should have used square-section wood, cardboard triangles and PVA adhesive to build simple structures such as a picture frame or a model bed. They need to have completed the activity 'Beams' (see page 15) before undertaking this activity so that they have knowledge of the following principles:
▲ triangulation;
▲ the depth of a beam is related to its strength;
▲ a bridge needs to be stable, and should therefore have a wide base.

### Key background information

The aim of this activity is to consolidate some of the basic concepts of structures. It is important that these features are emphasised and realised in any design that the children work on. It is very easy to build a bridge to span a small gap using enormous amounts of material and adhesives, but the children will learn very little about structure. An alternative approach would be to strictly limit the amount of wood and adhesive available, but this could be too restricting for children of this age.

### Vocabulary

Beam, stability, triangulation.

### Preparation

You will need to prepare a 'site' for the bridge. Ideally, this would be a scene made out of papier mâché to show clearly the gap that needs to be spanned. Alternatively, some bricks, separated by a short distance, will suffice. The choice of

'gap' almost directly relates to the amount of material that will be used. Wood often comes in 600mm lengths. Cutting this in half provides lengths which can be used easily to span a gap of 250mm. (Setting the gap at 300mm would mean a huge increase in the amount of wood used, with no advantage to the activity itself. Therefore, in this, and many other activities, it is worthwhile thinking carefully about the dimensions you select.)

### Resources needed

Pictures of beam bridges, square-section wood (each group will probably need five pieces 600mm long), cardboard triangles, PVA adhesive, masking tape, saw, ruler, bench hook, G-cramp.

### What to do

Remind children about the ideas of triangulation, stability and depth of beam. Show them a number of different types of beam bridge. The simplest beam bridge would be a plank from one side of a stream to another. The earliest origins of one would probably be a tree falling across from one side of a river to the other.

Explain that they are going to build a bridge to span a gap of 250mm. It should be as strong as possible and, if care is taken, it is quite possible to build a bridge that will withstand the weight of a child – or adult! The children must be accurate in cutting and gluing if this is to be a high quality product that can withstand large loads.

Points to emphasise are:
▲ close contact between the wood edges (PVA adhesive does not work effectively when it has to fill gaps – see Figure 1.5 below);
▲ very thin layers of PVA adhesive should be used;
▲ use of appropriate shapes of cardboard for reinforcing joints – not just triangles;
▲ use of masking tape to keep the pieces in place while the adhesive is setting;
▲ children should have a clear plan, for example, complete one side, then the other, then join them both together.

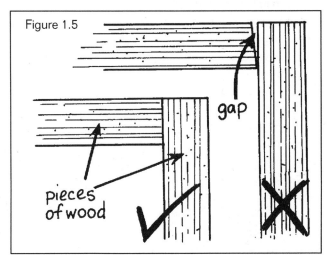

Figure 1.5

gap

pieces of wood

Encourage them to draw designs and to annotate their diagrams. They should also produce a detailed plan showing what materials and tools they will need and which member of the group will be responsible for each part of the task. The bridges should not be tested on the same day as they are completed – leave time for all the joints to dry. Avoid loading the bridges to destruction. It is very de-motivating to spend hours on an activity only to see it destroyed in seconds! Most structures will withstand a few bricks and it is generally clear which ones are strong enough to go for the ultimate test! (That is a child or adult standing on it.)

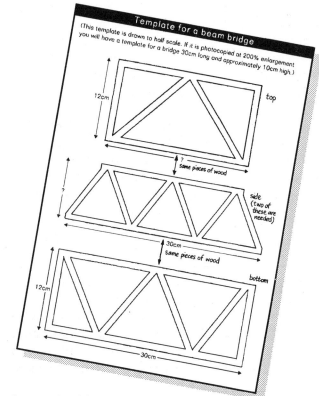

### Suggestion(s) for extension
Children could be encouraged to research, using CD-ROMs and other resources, different types of bridges and to build models of these as well.

### Suggestion(s) for support
Photocopiable sheet 110 provides a template of a typical beam bridge. This can be given to children who would have difficulty in designing and making their own bridge to match given specifications.

### Assessment opportunities
This activity gives an opportunity to assess children's planning and organisation. Have they made a step-by-step plan of the approach they intend to take? Do they follow it?

### Display ideas
A small papier mâché scene of a river and river bank could be built, and each group's bridge could be put into place on display for a short period of time.

### Reference to photocopiable sheet
Sheet 110 is a basic template with measurement specifications for a simple beam bridge. It can be used as support material to assist those children who are having difficulty designing their own bridge.

## GEODESICS · FPT

*To develop the skills and techniques appropriate for building a structure from artstraws, pipe cleaners and sheet material.*

†† *Working in pairs.*

🕐 *Three one-hour sessions.*

⚠ *Take care when using a hot glue gun. Alternative adhesives such as PVA or non-solvent based clear adhesive may be used.*

### Previous skills/knowledge needed
Children should already have examined a wide range of structures and noticed their main features.

### Key background information
Triangles are very important when building structures. Four lengths of wood, drilled and bolted at the corners to form a square can easily be distorted to form a diamond shape, no matter how firmly you tighten the bolts. With three lengths of wood joined together in the form of a triangle, no distortion can take place. (See Figure 1.6.)

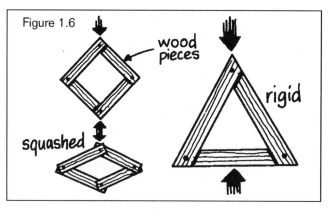

It was the architect Buckminster-Fuller who developed this idea of the structural strength of triangles and designed buildings made entirely from them. Once the framework is constructed, it can be covered with sheet materials cut out in the shape of equilateral triangles.

### Vocabulary
Geodesic or geodetic (both words can be used).

### Preparation
You will need photocopiable sheet 111, which shows the construction method to be used, as well as a picture of a completed geodesic dome. You will also need materials to

demonstrate the construction technique and a completed model with some of the dome covered in sheet material (for extension activity). Cut the artstraws into three equal lengths.

With reference to the group size suggested above, this activity would also lend itself to larger groups, if the activity was to be a focus for collaborative working. The time could be reduced accordingly.

### Resources needed
Jumbo artstraw pieces, pipe cleaners, thin cardboard (possibly other sheet material such as foamboard or corraflute), scissors, ruler, hot glue gun (or alternative adhesives), a copy of photocopiable sheet 111 for each child.

### What to do
Remind the children of the importance of the triangle shape in structures. Tell them about the architect Buckminster-Fuller who designed buildings made entirely out of triangles. Show them your completed model and explain that this is the sort of basic building they are going to make. Show the children the materials they are going to use and explain how to join the straws together using short pieces of pipe cleaner. Joining the ends together with sticky tape gives neither a strong joint nor an aesthetically pleasing finish. A small drip of hot glue creates an effective joint, and it can also provide a neat finish. (See Figure 1.7.)

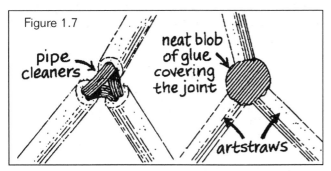

Figure 1.7

pipe cleaners

neat blob of glue covering the joint

artstraws

(Other adhesives, such as PVA or clear non-solvent based ones can be used, but it will take much longer to build the structure as each set of joints needs to dry before you attempt further ones. Using masking tape to keep the ends in place while they dry is a good idea, but it must be removed if you are going to produce a model of quality.) In parts of the structure there are going to be four or five straws joined together, so this is where the children will need to be patient and to work together as a team. It is important to emphasise quality of construction in the introduction. Give each child a copy of photocopiable sheet 111 for reference.

Encourage the children to make a small prototype before they begin their model so that they know how many triangles the structure will include. By continually making more and more equilateral triangles the structure can become very large and it is wise to limit this at an early stage. This can be done, either by providing a paper template showing the relative positions of the pieces, or by getting the children to build

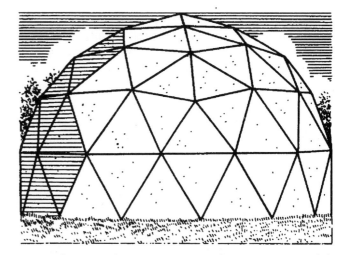

one to the same dimensions as your demonstration model. Either way, children should be discouraged from completing the base first, and then building upwards. The base determines the total number of equilateral triangles in the model, but it is very easy to incorporate extra triangles into the structure and to get a very strange shape. Once completed, the models could be tested for strength by hanging weights from the top of the structure. Watch out for straws which have been bent, and hence weakened, during construction. This is where the frame might fail.

### Suggestion(s) for extension
Groups could be asked to produce a building for a particular purpose and to decorate and finish it in an appropriate way, for example, a home, a leisure centre or a greenhouse. To do this the frames could be covered with sheet material in the form of equilateral triangles. A wide range of different sheet materials can be used, and the Jumbo artstraws can also be painted to enhance the look of the finished product.

### Suggestion(s) for support
Clear dimensions should be given, and a more directed approach should be taken. By giving the number of straws, their dimensions and a clear diagram of the structure it is possible for most children to have success with this activity.

### Assessment opportunities
This activity requires the children to measure accurately, and being a team activity also requires co-operation and a degree of discussion and planning.

### Opportunities for IT
If the children go on to finish their geodesic by covering the triangles they could use a drawing package to design the triangle shapes or to add a pattern or 'finish' to them. The shapes could be printed out on thin card or thick paper and cut out before being stuck onto the geodesic itself.

The children could use a word processor or desktop publishing package to create a 'for sale' poster for their geodesic. This could be extended by a 'for sale' brochure in

the style of an estate agent's leaflet. Pictures of the geodisec could be added, taken with a digital camera, created using a drawing or art package or scanned from the children's own drawings or photographs.

## Display ideas
Each group can identify a purpose for their particular geodesic, and the display can feature both the structure, a *For Sale* poster and leaflet.

## Reference to photocopiable sheet
Sheet 111 shows a diagram displaying the actual structure of a geodesic building, together with a close-up of how the straws are fixed together using pipe cleaners and a glue gun.

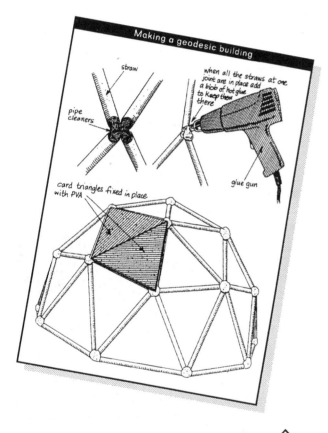

## OBSTACLE COURSE  FPT

*To develop skills and techniques associated with building structures from rolled up paper tubes. To design and make their own models using this construction medium.*

†† *Working in pairs.*

🕐 *Four one-hour sessions.*

⚠ *Ensure the children take care not to trap fingers when using the hole punch.*

## Previous skills/knowledge needed
Children should already be aware of the basic principles of stability and rigidity in structures.

## Key background information
The strength of materials can be altered by using them in different ways. For example, a kitchen roll tube can hold up a large weight if it is used as a pillar, but it is easily squashed by the same weight if it is on its side. (See Figure 1.8.)

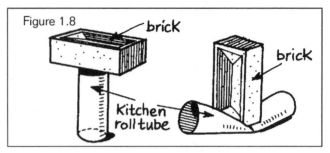

Similarly, sheets of paper and card can be folded in order to give them increased strength (see 'Beams' page 15). In this activity, children are going to turn sheets of paper into tubes which are able to withstand large forces. This gives children an opportunity to explore another construction technique which is relatively cheap. Models become more difficult to make when they require a lot of joins at one particular point in the structure.

## Preparation
Make the structure illustrated on photocopiable sheet 112.

## Resources needed
A4 paper, various thicknesses of dowel, brass paper fasteners, Plasticine, paper drill, heavy duty hole punch.

## What to do
Talk about obstacle courses and adventure playgrounds. Remind children of television programmes such as Gladiators and The Krypton Factor which involve obstacle courses of some kind. Get the children to look through catalogues containing playground equipment which will give them some ideas for obstacles they could make (ie a pictorial brainstorm). At this stage they need to be told the materials they are going to use. Use the paper tube model you have made as a sample, and then demonstrate how to make the tubes again following the instructions on photocopiable sheet 112.

The tubes can be made much stronger if they are wound round narrow dowel, but the disadvantages are that it is much more difficult to roll the tubes, and it can be hard to punch holes in the ends. There is therefore a compromise between ease of manufacture and strength. With some more able groups of children the relative advantages/disadvantages could be discussed. With other groups it would be more appropriate to let them make the wider but less sturdy tubes without additional discussion. Explain to the children that they can colour the paper using paint or felt-tipped pens, but that only a small part needs to be decorated, as the rest is rolled up in the tube. Coloured and textured papers can also be used to provide other finishes.

Now that the children are aware of the technique, they need to do more detailed designs of the structures they are going to build. If the intention is to make a complete obstacle course, then each group must be aware of size so that all the models are built to the same scale. They must be aware of the scale of the model. Hold a class discussion, using Plasticine figures as examples, and once a decision is reached, each group should have their own figure so that they are aware of scale throughout the designing and making. Construction kits would be an ideal modelling medium in which to try out their ideas. Groups can produce a large annotated diagram showing the ways in which their structure will be put together and what extra materials they will require, for example, netting, string, cardboard. The pairs then make their models according to their plans.

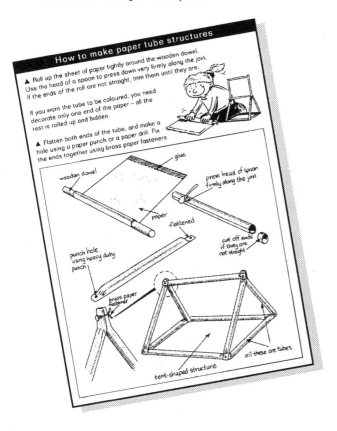

### Suggestion(s) for extension

Children could try incorporating mechanisms into these structures – either simple hinges or pulleys, or more complex mechanisms such as conveyor belts. While perfectly acceptable results can be achieved by using basic paper tubes, it is possible to incorporate a much wider range of other materials into the finished obstacle course. This technique, of linking rolled paper tubes, is also appropriate for making a wide range of other products including photo frames, novelty calendars and desk tidies. Instead of using brass paper fasteners, a stronger structure can be achieved by fitting brass eyelets in each hole and using nuts and bolts to fix the elements together. This, however, requires both extra strength and dexterity by the children.

### Suggestion(s) for support

Photocopiable sheet 112 gives a pictorial step-by-step guide to making and fixing the tubes together. Children may also find that a closer look at the simple model you have made helps them to produce their own structures.

### Assessment opportunities

As this is an activity that requires clear planning and the communication of these ideas to others in the class, a focus of evaluation could be on the overall effect of the obstacle course such as the consistency in scale throughout all the models; does it look as if it was planned by the group as a whole – has it got a range of different obstacles or are there five climbing nets?

### Display ideas

This could form the basis of a large display in the classroom or in the entrance to the school. Figures could be placed all over the model showing it 'in action', with explanations written by the children of how they were made.

### Reference to photocopiable sheet

Sheet 112 shows pictorially how the tubes are made, and how they are fixed together to produce a structure. It can be used to assist those children who have difficulty understanding what to do.

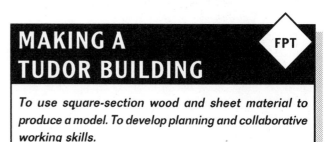

## MAKING A TUDOR BUILDING    FPT

*To use square-section wood and sheet material to produce a model. To develop planning and collaborative working skills.*

†† *Working in pairs.*

⏰ *Four one-hour sessions.*

⚠ *Take care when using saws and craft knives.*

### Previous skills/knowledge needed

This is an activity which should be undertaken by children who have already constructed simple structures using square-section wood and cardboard triangles. Children must be able to use a saw to cut the square-section wood, and a craft knife to cut the cardboard or foamboard. They need to be aware of the different types of buildings that existed in Tudor times. An understanding of scale from their work in mathematics is also necessary.

### Key background information

This activity links clearly into work which children will be doing in history on life in Tudor times. They should use their knowledge of this period of history when researching into the style of their particular house.

**DESIGN AND TECHNOLOGY**

## Preparation
Collect pictures of Tudor homes.

## Resources needed
A number of pictures of Tudor buildings, photocopiable sheets 113, 114 and 115 for each child, square-section wood, PVA adhesive, card or foamboard, straw, dark waterproof stain, saw, bench hook, G-cramp, craft knife, cutting mat, metal safety rule, paintbrush.

## What to do
Having undertaken work on the Tudors, the children should be introduced to the idea of producing a Tudor town or village. Show the pictures of Tudor buildings and highlight particularly the triangular shapes in the beams. Photocopiable sheet 113 gives illustrations of four different kinds of buildings: a barn, a town house, a 'shoppe' and a manor house. This activity will involve children in cutting square-section wood at angles other than 90 degrees. This activity requires considerable planning to ensure a quality finished product. It also requires discussion of scale if all the models are to form part of a display. Plasticine figures can be used to enable children to visualise the importance of each building being to the same scale – although not necessarily the same size.

Through discussion, each pair should decide on the type of building they are to construct. Planning is an integral part of this activity and rough sketches and an indication of the lengths of wood which are required should be produced first. The Tudor building planning sheet 115 should help to provide a structure for each pair's design. Each pair should discuss the way in which their building is to be constructed. Triangles should form an obvious part of the structure. One easy approach would be to produce the four walls of the building separately and then to glue them together. The roof would be constructed last. Tell the children to build the wooden structure first and then stick a sheet of card or foamboard behind the wood, enabling the wooden *beams* to show. In this way children are given an opportunity to measure materials, and design, in a limited way, their own building.

## Suggestion(s) for extension
Instead of painting the roof or using 'tiled' paper, children could produce a thatched effect using straw (drinking or real), glue and thread. More detail could be incorporated into the model with opening hinged windows and doors, transparent and bow-windows.

## Suggestion(s) for support
Photocopaible sheet 114 gives a structured approach to building the house. By using the templates which show the sizes and angles at which the wood needs to be cut, a perfectly satisfactory product can be produced.

## Assessment opportunities
This activity requires wood to be measured and cut very accurately, at very specific angles. It is also possible to assess how effectively the children have worked together as a group by talking to them both throughout and at the end of the activity.

## Opportunities for IT
The children could use a CD-ROM to help them research information on Tudor houses before starting the work. Alternatively they could use framework software such as My World 2 with the 'Design a 3D Tudor House' file to make a paper model of the house they are going to build using the wooden structure.

## Display ideas
All the models could be incorporated into a model of a Tudor village or town which could be displayed in a large area, such as the school entrance. If this were to become a prestige project, it could incorporate some electrical elements such as a glowing fire in one of the houses, or a tape of village sounds and music playing at the touch of a button.

## Reference to photocopiable sheets
Sheet 113 shows pictures of four different kinds of Tudor buildings. Sheet 114 gives construction details of one, relatively simple building, including templates for individual lengths of wood and can be used as a support material. Planning sheet 115 reminds children of the stages they need to go through.

DESIGN AND TECHNOLOGY

# Mechanisms

This section consists of activities relating to mechanisms, including simple levers, pulleys, cams, gears and some simple work on pneumatics.

These activities will also give children opportunities to:
▲ become familiar with ways of joining materials and components to allow movement;
▲ investigate mechanisms in everyday products;
▲ recognise different kinds of movement.

In terms of designing and making skills these activities will give children opportunities to identify what tools and materials they may need, and what to do with them in a given time sequence. They will also evaluate ideas (do they meet the needs of the users, for example). They will learn the skills of measuring, sawing, cutting accurately, assembling (construction kits, mock-ups) together with learning about the use of and skill involved in using paints, varnish, cladding, glasspaper and templates.

## LEARNING FROM OTHER PEOPLE'S WORK

**IDEA**

*To understand the importance of evaluating existing products before the children design and make their own.*

☨☨ *Working in pairs.*

🕐 *One-hour session.*

### Previous skills/knowledge needed

Experience of evaluating their own work both when it is finished and throughout the processes of designing and making.

### Key background information

Why re-invent the wheel? It is important that we do not expect children to do all their designing and making from scratch. A useful starting point for many activities is to let children look in considerable detail at existing products and find out how they work. They are then able to use this information in their own designing and making work. It is also important that any IDEA (investigative, disassemble and evaluative activity) is linked to some future focused practical task or design and make assignment. There is little point in investigating, disassembling and evaluating clocks and then building a vehicle! The focus for this particular activity is, therefore, mechanical toys as it gives an appropriate introduction to the activity 'An advertising toy' on page 27. However, the structure and many of the questions within this task are appropriate for the evaluation of many existing products.

### Vocabulary

Evaluating.

### Preparation

Ask children to bring in some mechanical toys. Create an exhibition of them for a week or so prior to the project taking place. Alternatively, a visit to a toy museum could be arranged. A supply of books containing pictures of mechanical toys would also be useful but there is no adequate replacement for the real toys that the children can get their hands on.

### Resources needed

A wide selection of toys brought in from home and/or supplied by the school. Books containing photographs of mechanical toys.

### What to do

The children will have had opportunities to look at the toys for the previous week. Now distribute one toy to each pair and ask them to look at it in detail. Ask them to brainstorm a list of questions which they would like answered about their particular toy (photocopiable sheet 116 provides some questions as a guide to what the children should come up

with). After ten minutes let the pairs make groups of six and produce a composite list of questions. Then get each group to share their questions with the rest of the class so that you have a class list of questions. These will be useful starting points when the children come to make their own toy.

Each pair should now look at the mechanical part of the toy then explain to the rest of the class something about the mechanism which they have discovered. This might be that part of it moves up and down as the wheels go round, or that it has a large spring on it which allows part of it to move up and down. Some of this information may be useful when the children come to design their own toy, or indeed, some other mechanism.

| Evaluating toys |
|---|
| Name _____  Date _____ |
| What shape is it? |
| What does it feel like? |
| What is it made of? |
| What materials might we use to make it today? |
| How is it made? |
| By hand or machine? |
| What tools would be needed? |
| Does it move? |
| What makes it move? |
| Does it make a noise? |
| Who would play with it? |
| Where and when? |
| Is it more fun to play with if it costs a lot? |
| Is it played with by boys and girls? |
| What aged children will play with it? |
| Is it safe? (CE mark) |
| Does it need a battery? |
| Your questions |

### Suggestion(s) for extension

Having identified particular mechanisms, children could research in more detail how they work. Some of the activities in this section could then develop from their initial findings.

### Suggestion(s) for support

Photocopiable sheet 116 provides some questions to prompt the children in making up their own. They can also attempt to answer the questions.

### Assessment opportunities

This activity provides a focus for the evaluation of existing products. The questions which individual groups come up with will provide useful evidence.

### Opportunities for IT

The pairs of children could use a word processor or desktop publishing package to write and present their list of questions about the toy they have been examining. The could be printed

**DESIGN AND TECHNOLOGY**

out in the form of a stand up label (folded A4 sheet) to be displayed alongside the class display of toys. Let the children experiment with different fonts, styles and borders to make the label more interesting. They will also need to decide where to place the text on the page so that it is the right way up when the printed sheet is folded in half!

The children's work could be extended by writing an explanation of how the mechanism works and adding this to the list of questions. This might need to be spread over a longer period of time and children should save their work so that they can retrieve it at a later date.

The children could also use encyclopaedia CD-ROMs to research information about their toy or mechanism.

### Display ideas
Add the questions which the class have devised to the existing exhibition of toys. For some of the toys give a list of answers.

### Reference to photocopiable sheet
Sheet 116 contains a list of questions to assist in evaluating toys. This can be used to help assess whether the children have asked the right sort of questions, or as a support sheet to help those children who are having difficulty making up their own. The answers to the questions should provoke further questions.

## A PNEUMATIC CAR PARK BARRIER  `FPT`

*To develop children's understanding of pneumatics. To build a simple model incorporating these ideas.*
†† *Working in pairs.*
🕐 *Two one-hour sessions.*
⚠ *Ensure the children take care when using the saw to cut square-section wood.*

### Previous skills/knowledge needed
Children should have carried out simple pneumatics work using balloons, plastic tubing and washing-up liquid containers. They should also have made simple structures using square-section wood, cardboard triangles and PVA adhesive and be aware of the principles of simple levers.

### Key background information
Pneumatics and hydraulics are very similar concepts. In a pneumatics system a gas, usually compressed air, is used to transmit movement. In hydraulics a liquid, usually some kind of oil, is used. These ideas can be simulated in models at Key Stage 2 by using syringes connected together with plastic tubing. If you are simulating a pneumatic system, you will be using air, and if it is hydraulics then the syringes and tubing should be full of water.

In the simple models which are usually undertaken at Key Stage 2, either basic principle could be used, but pneumatics is to be recommended as it is far less messy! The only time when hydraulics may be an appropriate system is when the load which needs to be moved is quite large. This activity only considers pneumatics. Normally you will use two different sizes of syringe. This allows the plunger of a large syringe to be moved a small distance causing the plunger in a small syringe to move a much greater distance.

### Vocabulary
Pneumatics, hydraulics, fulcrum, pivot, compressible.

### Preparation
Make a simple see-saw model out of square-section wood so that you can revise the children's previous work on levers in the context of their work on pneumatics. (See Figure 2.1.)

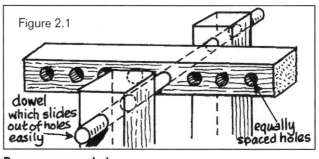

Figure 2.1

dowel which slides out of holes easily

equally spaced holes

### Resources needed
Two small syringes, one large syringe, a T-piece and a 50cm length of plastic tubing for each pair of children, square-section wood, card triangles, PVA adhesive, saw, bench hook, G-cramp, plastic tube cutter, acrylic paint or water-based varnish, one copy of photocopiable sheet 117, paper.

### What to do
Ask the children to think about the noises they hear when a bus puts it brakes on, or when the sliding door of a bus opens or closes. Focus in on the hiss of escaping air. These are examples of pneumatics systems, where air is used to make things move. (The brakes moving onto the wheels and the doors opening.) Each pair should now go through the investigations on photocopiable sheet 117. Provide them with the resources listed above.

After they have completed the sheet, summarise the significant points in a class discussion. In particular note the following features:

▲ air can be squashed (it is compressible);

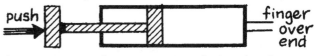

push                    finger over end

▲ air is springy – if one syringe is pushed in, the plunger in the second syringe comes out;

push                    tube

▲ if one syringe is pulled out, the plunger in the second syringe moves inwards;

▲ small movements in a large syringe give larger movements in a small syringe.

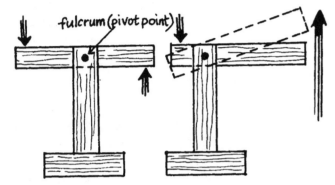

Now show the children the model of the see-saw. As you push down on one side the other side goes up.

Take out the piece of dowel (the fulcrum), and move it along to the left. As you push down on the left the right-hand side moves much further.

fulcrum (pivot point)

Suggest to the children that it looks a bit like a car park barrier. Now move the dowel further to the left. Ask how they could use the work they did on pneumatics to control the gate from a distance. As the children offer suggestions you will gradually get to the situation of fixing the small syringe near one end of the barrier, so that as it is forced down, the barrier rises. Emphasise how the outer casing of the syringe needs to be fixed to the wooden frame, allowing the inner piston to move freely. The barrier will close automatically because there is more weight to the right of the fulcrum (pivot point). The children should now have a basic idea of how to complete their model of a car park barrier.

Ask them to look at car park barriers for ideas. Remind them that they often have a holder for the barrier when it is in the down position. They should complete initial designs and then build their models. Restrict the available materials to ensure that they all cut wood and dowel, and drill holes accurately. The model could be coloured with water-based varnish or acrylic paint both of which can give a reasonable finish. Acrylic paint can give a reasonable finish.

When the barriers are complete, each child should do a presentation drawing. This can be annotated to show important features of the design such as the materials used, reasons for their selection and the ways in which the components are fixed together. It should also highlight particular problems which occurred during the making. This is a good strategy to make children think about the process of evaluation throughout an activity.

## Suggestion(s) for extension
Children could be asked to make a model of their own choice which incorporates a pneumatic movement. With some groups it might be better to restrict this choice – a sliding door is a relatively simple and relevant application. It might be appropriate to expect a more detailed design from the children before they start making this alternative model.

## Suggestion(s) for support
For children who have difficulty in visualising what the model will look like, give out the more detailed photocopiable sheet 118. This is a presentation drawing of the type you will expect most children to produce. It can be used, therefore, as an example for those children who are unsure of the nature of an annotated diagram. However, it would be unwise to give all children sheet 118 as it will remove the limited design element from the activity.

## Assessment opportunities
This activity gives an opportunity to assess the children's ability to evaluate as they are undertaking a project. The annotations on the presentation drawing provide the evidence.

## Opportunities for IT
The children could use the computer to make an annotated drawing of their car park barrier. They could use a drawing package or a simple CAD (computer aided design) package such as My World 2 framework software and the CAD file.

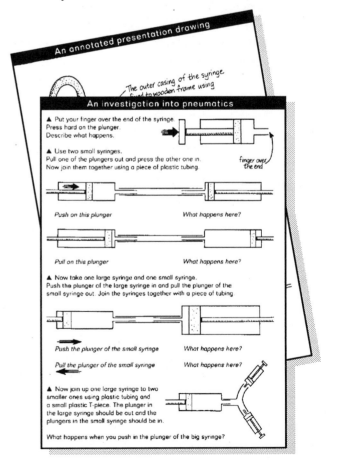

## Display ideas

This activity would give children an opportunity to produce an annotated diagram of their model, clearly identifying how they solved particular problems and the materials and techniques they used. These can be displayed together with the completed models.

## Reference to photocopiable sheets

Sheet 117 leads the children through some activities covering the basic principles of pneumatics. Sheet 118 provides a annotated presentation drawing of a car park barrier. It can be used to help children who are having difficulties with their own design, and also provides an example of what an annotated presentation drawing actually is.

## AN ADVERTISING TOY ◄ FPT

*To develop children's understanding of cams.*
*To design and make a simple moving toy, incorporating cams, which could be used to advertise a local event.*
*To understand the purpose and value of prototyping.*

†† *Working in pairs.*

⏲ *Three one-hour sessions.*

⚠ *Take care when using a saw to cut wood. Make sure the children are closely supervised if they use a craft knife for cutting sheet material. They should use a metal safety rule and a cutting mat.*

## Previous skills/knowledge needed

Children should be familiar with working with wood and sheet material such as card, foamboard or corrugated plastic sheet. Preferably they should have undertaken the activity 'Learning from other people's work' (page 24) where there was a focus on toys incorporating wheels and cams. They should also be familiar with a technical construction kit so that they can use them to build prototypes of their models.

## Key background information

A cam is used to change a turning movement into an up and down movement. The easiest sort of cam to make is a wheel where the axle is not at the centre.

## Vocabulary

Cam, follower, pear-shaped cam, off-centred cam, prototype.

## Preparation

You need a simple visual aid to illustrate the principle behind cams as explained above. The one in Figure 2.2 above can be made out of corrugated plastic, wooden wheels, brass paper fasteners and square-section wood. It is probably easiest to create cams from wooden wheels. An electric 'shaper' saw can be used effectively for this. In this activity, children will need to use only an off-centred, circular cam.

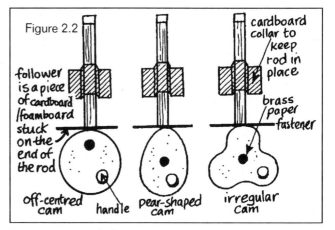

Figure 2.2

## Resources needed

Sturdy cardboard boxes (shoeboxes are ideal), wooden wheels, dowel, paper drill, Jumbo artstraws, cardboard, scissors, plastic tubing, plastic tube cutters, suitable toys incorporating cams, books containing pictures of these sorts of toys, technical construction kit, copy of photocopiable sheet 119 for each child.

## What to do

Remind children of the mechanical toys they have seen (if the activity on page 24 has not been done, then make sure they have time to see the toys available). In particular, focus upon toys where turning a handle causes something to move up and down. Show the children your display model. Show how the cams can turn round and make the followers move up and down. The follower is the part which follows the shape of the cam. Figure 2.2 shows three types of cam – an off-centred cam, a pear-shaped cam and an irregular cam. The irregular cam needs to have a smooth shape otherwise the follower might get stuck – the rod linked to the irregular cam moves in an uneven way. The pear-shaped cam rises for about one-quarter of a turn, and then keeps the rod lower and steady for the remaining three-quarters of the rotation. The off-centred cam moves up and down all the time – there is no period where it stays level.

Explain to the children that for almost all the uses for which they may want to use cams, an off-centred circle will work well. This means that wooden wheels drilled with an off-centred hole are usually most effective in this sort of application. Photocopiable sheet 119 gives a step by step explanation of simple cams, with a few of the drawbacks.

Ask the children to suggest ways in which a cam could be used, for example, the hat of a clown moving up and down. Explore with them how this would actually work by holding or fixing pieces of card to your model to represent a hat and a face. This will illustrate the principle of prototyping – trying out your ideas practically, in a rough form, before producing a proper version. Now let the children build a simple cam mechanism using a technical construction kit. The guides which go with the kit usually include pictures and diagrams showing an example of a cam.

**DESIGN AND TECHNOLOGY**

Once they have explored cams, show the children the materials which are available for their activity. The purpose of this toy will be to advertise a local event or shop, for example, a visit by a travelling circus or a forthcoming theatre event. In their pairs they should brainstorm some ideas. Each group then decides what their toy will be like and works out what the moving part is going to be. It could come from the top of a box (see Figure 2.3).

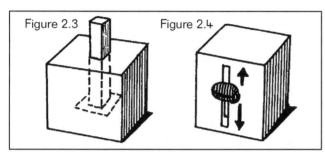

Figure 2.3    Figure 2.4

It could slide up the front of the box for something like 'the mouse ran up the clock' advertising a pet shop (see Figure 2.4). Each pair will be using very similar materials, but their designs will be different. Roughly sketched ideas and paper, card and construction kit prototypes should be the focus of this activity. (Children need not make the actual models if time is limited, instead they can make them for an extension of the activity. However, the finished model is part of the assessment process and display idea.)

### Suggestion(s) for extension
The model could be extended to incorporate a number of cams on the same axle so that two up and down movements occur (see figure 2.4A). A pull along toy could be made which incorporates a cam on the wheel and axle. Children who are designing and making more advanced models can use photocopiable sheet 120 to annotate and extend the design to a more sophisticated level.

Figure 2.4a    this going down as...    ...this going up

### Suggestion(s) for support
Photocopiable sheet 120 provides some suggestions of how cams can be used to create movement. This sheet can be used by children who are having difficulties devising their own ideas (they can basically make a copy of the design).

### Assessment opportunities
This activity gives opportunities to value the importance of prototyping and to assess how effectively it contributed to the quality of the finished product.

### Display ideas
To emphasise the importance of prototyping, this display should consist of the prototype shown together with the completed model. Children could be asked to see what changes they see between the two models. Alternatively, photographs of the prototypes could be taken and the display could focus upon matching the prototype to the finished product.

### Reference to photocopiable sheets
Sheet 119 shows the basic principles of cams. Sheet 120 shows a possible way of incorporating cams into a model and can be used for extension or support purposes.

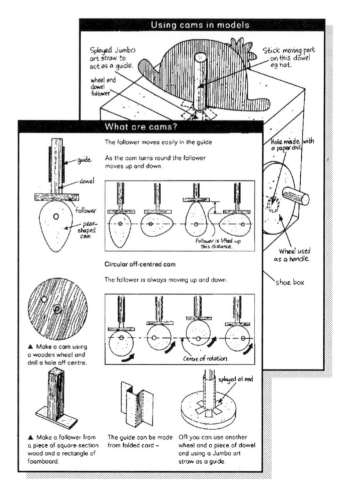

# THE COW JUMPED OVER THE MOON!

**FPT**

*To understand the basic features of simple levers. To make a model which incorporates simple levers set in the context of a nursery rhyme. To follow instructions and concentrate on overall quality of the finished product.*

†† *Working individually.*

🕐 *Three one-hour sessions.*

⚠ *Children should wear goggles when they are using a 'shaper' saw. They should be carefully instructed in its use before using it themselves for the first time. Use spray adhesive (Spray Mount) in a well-ventilated room, and avoid spraying near eyes.*

## Previous skills/knowledge needed

Children will need to have experience working with simple levers made out of card and brass paper fasteners.

## Key background information

This activity will not only help children to develop their understanding of levers, but also it is designed to enable them to experience a wide range of techniques in a very focused way, which will enhance their making skills in the future. There is limited scope for creativity in this activity, although the decoration of the background scene can be left for each child.

## Vocabulary

Lever, fulcrum, pivot.

## Preparation

You need a completed model using a simple lever mechanism of a cow jumping over the moon (see photocopiable sheet 121). You will also need to have printed out computer clip art pictures of a moon and a cow for each child. If the children are familiar with the procedure, you may wish them to print out their own clip art images at their chosen size.

## Resources needed

Foamboard, brass paper fasteners, lolly sticks, water-based varnish, spray adhesive, PVA adhesive, computer clip art pictures of moon and cow, model of cow jumping over moon, goggles, copy of photocopiable sheet 121 for each child.

## What to do

Ask the children to imagine that they were going to teach the nursery rhyme 'Hey diddle diddle' to some four- to five-year-olds. How could they make it a little bit more interesting for them? Show the children what happens when the lever is moved backwards and forwards on your completed model. Remind them of the terms pivot (and/or fulcrum). Disconnect the lever from the brass paper fastener and connect it to a different hole. The cow now moves in a different way. The children can experience this change for themselves when they have completed the activity.

Give each child photocopiable sheet 121 which gives step by step instructions of how to make the model. Give a demonstration of how to use the 'shaper' saw safely – remind children to wear goggles. They should not rush to cut out the shape but do it slowly and carefully. The cutting edge of the blade faces forwards – the cow and the moon shape should be manoeuvred round so that the cutting edge of the blade is in the right direction. As the children build their models, focus their attention on the importance of finishing and the quality of presentation of the final model. Talk about the following:

▲ the use of glasspaper to smooth edges;

▲ the use of small quantities of PVA adhesive to avoid unnecessary 'blobs' of glue;

▲ making the holes equally spaced and along the central line of the lolly sticks;

▲ hiding the head of the brass paper fastener under the moon.

## Suggestion(s) for extension

More able children could devise similar scenes for other nursery rhymes. Computer clip art collections offer vast ranges of suitable images which can be printed out at any appropriate size. Alternatively, children can use line drawings from colouring books or draw the pictures themselves.

## Suggestion(s) for support

Letting the children have the finished model which you used at the introduction to the activity will provide extra assistance.

## Assessment opportunities

This activity enables you to see how effectively children can follow instructions. It also gives opportunities to assess the accuracy of measuring, intricate cutting and the quality of the finishing.

## Opportunities for IT

The children could use a drawing or art package to design their own background for the model. They could either draw the whole background for themselves or make use of suitable pictures from commercial clip art collections. In the latter case the children will need to know how to find pictures from the clip art, import them into the drawing package, position them on the page and re-size them to fit in with the rest of their background picture.

## Display ideas

The models can be mounted on the wall so that the levers can be moved and the cows can be seen to jump. If it is decided that the activity should be taken further with scenes from different nursery rhymes, then obviously the display will become more interesting.

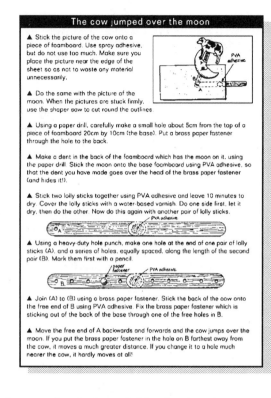

**The cow jumped over the moon**

▲ Stick the picture of the cow onto a piece of foamboard. Use spray adhesive, but do not use too much. Make sure you place the picture near the edge of the sheet so as not to waste any material unnecessarily.

▲ Do the same with the picture of the moon. When the pictures are stuck firmly, use the shaper saw to cut round the outlines.

▲ Using a paper drill, carefully make a small hole about 5cm from the top of a piece of foamboard 20cm by 10cm (the base). Put a brass paper fastener through the hole to the back.

▲ Make a dent in the back of the foamboard which has the moon on it, using the paper drill. Stick the moon onto the base foamboard using PVA adhesive, so that the dent you have made goes over the head of the brass paper fastener (and hides it!).

▲ Stick two lolly sticks together using PVA adhesive and leave 10 minutes to dry. Cover the lolly sticks with a water-based varnish. Do one side first, let it dry, then do the other. Now do this again with another pair of lolly sticks.

▲ Using a heavy-duty hole punch, make one hole at the end of one pair of lolly sticks (A), and a series of holes, equally spaced, along the length of the second pair (B). Mark them first with a pencil.

▲ Join (A) to (B) using a brass paper fastener. Stick the back of the cow onto the free end of B using PVA adhesive. Fix the brass paper fastener which is sticking out of the back of the base through one of the free holes in B.

▲ Move the free end of A backwards and forwards and the cow jumps over the moon. If you put the brass paper fastener in the hole on B farthest away from the cow, it moves a much greater distance. If you change it to a hole much nearer the cow, it hardly moves at all!

### Reference to photocopiable sheet

Sheet 121 shows the step-by-step instructions for making the scene.

## GEAR WHEELS   ◆ FPT

*To make a simple gear wheel. To understand the basic principles of linking gears together.*

†† *Working in groups of three.*

🕐 *Two one-hour sessions.*

▲ *If children make their own wheels, they should be warned that the blade and pointer on the compass cutter are very sharp.*

### Previous skills/knowledge needed

Children need to have used a paper drill for producing holes in cardboard and be familiar with the use of brass paper fasteners as a form of fixing.

### Key background information

This focused practical task aims to give children the opportunity to make a gear wheel of their own and to investigate how simple gear wheels can change both the direction and speed of rotation.

### Vocabulary

Gear, cog, driver, follower, idler, mesh, rotation.

### Preparation

Collect some drawings/photographs/posters of machines which incorporate gears, as well as a few everyday objects which have easily seen gears in them. Prepare one sheet of thick card with holes placed in the appropriate places, and measurements marked clearly on the reverse. (This will help children who may have difficulty measuring accurately.) Prepare a board complete with gear wheels to use as a model but do not let them see it until they are making up their own boards. You could also use a compass cutter to cut your own wheels out of thick card if you prefer.

### Resources needed

For this activity you will need a gear jig, match sticks and cardboard wheels of a range of sizes and PVA adhesive. Each group of three will need at least one gear jig, six cardboard wheels – two each of 25mm, 51mm and 63mm diameter, at least one container of PVA adhesive and three spreaders, a pile of matchsticks, three large brass paper fasteners, a paper drill and a thick sheet of A4 sized card suitable for mounting the gears. Copies of photocopiable sheets 122 and 123 for each child.

### What to do

Introduce the subject of gears with a whole class discussion on the topic. Have available the pictures of machines and everyday objects (see 'Preparation' above) as a stimulus. Children will probably be familiar with gears on bikes, and know that there are gears in cars. A food whisk and a hand drill both have gearing systems.

Explain to the children that they are going to make some gear wheels, and then find out what they can be used for. Each group is to make three different-sized gear wheels – each child can make one of their own.

Demonstrate the basic principles they are to use (see photocopiable sheet 122).

▲ cardboard wheel placed into the jig;

▲ small amount of PVA adhesive spread over the wheel;

▲ matchsticks placed carefully in pairs in the jig – some will need to be cut (or broken) to size;

▲ small amount of PVA adhesive spread over the matches, where they are in contact with the cardboard;

▲ second cardboard wheel placed on top of the matches;

▲ leave to dry for ten minutes before carefully removing the gear wheel from the jig.

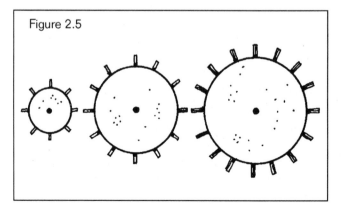

Figure 2.5

**DESIGN AND TECHNOLOGY**

Each group can then make three different size gear wheels (see Figure 2.5). A typical jig will allow you to make eight-teeth (25mm wheel), twelve-teeth (51mm wheel) and sixteen-teeth (63mm wheel) gear wheels. The matches for the smallest gear wheel will have to be broken in half in order to fit.

Once the children have made their wheels provide each group with a thick sheet of cardboard on which their gear wheels can be mounted. They will then be able to undertake a simple investigation.

Photocopiable sheet 123 shows exactly where the holes need to be drilled, using a paper drill, so that the gear wheels mesh together. One board should already be prepared so that children can use it as a guide. Children work through the sheet recording their answers. After completing this activity they should be aware that:

▲ two gears which mesh together travel in opposite directions;

▲ an idler gear can be used to change the direction of rotation;

▲ a small driver will travel faster than the larger follower;

▲ a large driver will travel slower than the smaller follower.

## Suggestion(s) for extension

The children now have one gear wheel that they can incorporate in a model of their own design. (See the activity 'A zoetrope' below.)

## Suggestion(s) for support

Let the children work in mixed ability groups of three. Have some gear wheels already made up to demonstrate to the children. Have a board made up to show how the gears can mesh together.

## Assessment opportunities

The children's responses to photocopiable sheet 123 will provide you with evidence of their understanding of the basic concepts of gearing. The quality of each child's gear wheel will provide you with evidence of their practical skills in the careful placing of the matches in the jig, and the economical and effective use of PVA adhesive.

## Opportunities for IT

The children could use a CD-ROM to research information on machines that use gears. They could also use a word processor to write labels for their gear boards. The labels could include clip art illustrations of machines which incorporate gears.

## Display ideas

If the children label the boards with suitable questions, they could be used as interactive teaching aids for other children in the school. For example:

'Which way does gear wheel B travel if you turn gear wheel A in the direction of the red arrow?'

'Now see if you were right.'

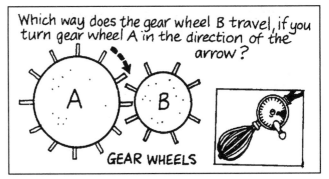

Which way does the gear wheel B travel, if you turn gear wheel A in the direction of the arrow?

GEAR WHEELS

## Reference to photocopiable sheets

Sheet 122 shows the process of making the gears in the gear jig. Sheet 123 leads the children through an investigation into how gears work.

An investigation into gears

# A ZOETROPE   FPT

*To gain an understanding of how gears can transfer motion through a right angle. To use this knowledge to build a hand-operated zoetrope.*

†† *Working in groups of three or four.*

🕐 *Five one-hour sessions.*

⚠ *Take care when using a saw. Make sure the craft knife is used with a metal safety rule and a cutting mat.*

## Previous skills/knowledge needed

Children should have a basic understanding of gears. In this activity the gears are used to change the angle of rotation through only 90 degrees. Children should be familiar with construction a basic cuboid structure using square-section wood, cardboard triangles and PVA adhesive.

## Key background information

The zoetrope shows moving images because of the persistence of vision. That is, each image remains on the retina of the eye for a short time – this allows individual images to merge into a movinig scene. Without persistence of vision all you would see is a series of individual pictures with no apparent movement. The zoetrope is a more sophisticated form of flip book. Gears can be used to change motion through 90 degrees. This is a relatively complex model to build and requires considerable skill, although it is within the capabilities of Key Stage 2 children who have achieved a good level of practical skill.

## Vocabulary

Zoetrope, thaumatrope, persistence of vision.

## Preparation

Ideally have access to an original zoetrope. If this is not possible, you probably need a completed model, although you may decide not to show it to the children at this stage. Photographs, and other examples of Victorian optical toys could be used to set the scene. Alternatively, a visit to a toy museum or the Museum of the Moving Image in London would give children the experience of seeing Victorian optical toys.

## Resources needed

Square-section wood, cardboard triangles, PVA adhesive, wooden wheels, cardboard wheels, black cardboard, matchsticks and/or dowel, Lynx gear jig, saw, bench hook, G-cramp, craft knife, cutting board, metal safety rule, paint, pencils and pens, copies of photocopiable sheet 124, one for each child.

## What to do

Using the above visit to a museum or the photographs, initiate a discussion about Victorian optical toys. Make up a simple series of stick figures at the top corners of pages in an exercise book to give the children the idea of apparent movement obtained by quickly flicking through a whole series of stationary but slightly different pictures. (Children can also make a simple thaumatrope – a disc with different pictures on each side which appear to merge when the disc is spun on thread or elastic.)

Tell the children that they are going to build a model of an optical toy called a 'zoetrope'. Give the groups a copy of photocopiable sheet 124 which shows the basic construction details of a zoetrope. Children should be encouraged to plan carefully how they go about building their model and be given a few guidelines.

The structure should be built in sections, for example, the base should be built first and then allowed to dry. Holes should be drilled in wood before it is stuck in place. Great care must be taken in the placement of the gear wheels, axles and handle. The gear wheels must be supported vertically and horizontally, and they should mesh approximately half way along their length (see Figure 2.6).

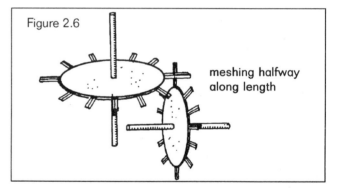

Figure 2.6

meshing halfway along length

The gear jigs can either use matchsticks or lengths of dowel. Matchsticks are cheaper, but dowels give a much more effective gear wheel. In this model both gear wheels are the same size. The reason for using gears is that the handle turned in a vertical plane can be used to rotate the zoetrope turntable in a horizontal plane. It would be possible to use differently sized gear wheels (a large one on the handle and a small one on the turntable base) if you wanted the zoetrope to rotate more quickly.

The children do the following:

▲ copy the drawings onto a sheet of white paper 40cm long and 8cm high;

▲ stick this sequence of drawings onto a piece of black card 40cm long and 10cm high;

▲ using a craft knife, metal safety rule and cutting mat, cut out a slit between every picture;

▲ roll the card into a circle and fix it to the turntable;

They can now look through the slits, and turn the handle. They should see a cartoon figure moving.

## Suggestion(s) for extension

With care, it is possible to power the zoetrope using a motor. Groups could produce their own cartoon sequences rather than using the one illustrated on photocopiable sheet 124.

## Suggestions for support

To make the activity a little simpler, plastic gears could be used rather than home-made wooden ones. A high degree of accuracy is required in producing a working zoetrope, and it may be that some alternative, such as a roundabout, could be built on the turntable device.

## Assessment opportunities

Considerable planning is needed if a model of this type is to be completed, and is able to work effectively. This activity gives an opportunity for this concentration on planning by the children to be assessed.

## Opportunities for IT

The children knowledge of the idea of moving images could be extended by their trying out some of the more recent software which enables them to make simple animated sequences on the computer screen.

They could also use a CD-ROM to research information on other Victorian optical toys, possibly using a word processor to write their own accounts of them. In this work the children may need to be shown how to save text from a CD-ROM in ASCII (American standard code for information interchange) format and then reload it into a word processor for refining and editing. The children can often import pictures from the CD-ROM in a similar way.

## Display ideas

The zoetropes could be displayed together with other Victorian optical toys, such as a thaumatrope and flip book. Any extra cartoon sequences made by the children who attempted the extension activity, could also be displayed.

## Reference to photocopiable sheet

Sheet 124 includes details of how to make the wooden framework, the gears and the zoetrope pictures.

---

# A CONVEYOR BELT   FPT

*To gain an understanding of the principles of simple pulleys. To make use of these ideas while designing and making a conveyor belt system.*

†† *Working in groups of four.*

🕐 *Three one-hour sessions.*

⚠ *Make sure children know how to saw wood safely using a bench hook and a G-cramp to provide a secure sawing surface.*

---

## Previous skills/knowledge needed

The children should be familiar with the use of square-section wood, cardboard triangles and PVA adhesive. They should also be familiar with the principles behind wheels and axles.

## Key background information

This activity requires children to use simple pulleys and a belt drive. More detailed investigations with pulleys are carried out in the activity 'Making a buggy' (see page 86). A pulley is basically a wheel with a belt attached to it which is connected to another wheel. They usually have grooves in them so that it is not easy for the belt (usually a rubber band) to slip out. In this activity children will be looking at ways of making pulleys out of different materials.

## Vocabulary

Drive pulley, driven pulley.

## Preparation

A week or so before starting this activity ask children to bring in any illustrations of conveyor belts or moving walkways they can find. You will need a few of the examples of home-made pulleys which are shown on photocopiable sheet 125.

## Resources needed

Square-section wood, dowel, cardboard triangles, plastic tubing, flexible corrugated cardboard, cardboard, foamboard or corrugated plastic, drills and drill bits, saw, bench hook, G-cramp, plastic tube cutter, selection of materials suitable for large pulleys (aluminium drinks cans, wooden wheels, cotton reels, coffee jar lids), copies of photocopiable sheets 125 and 126 for at least one per group.

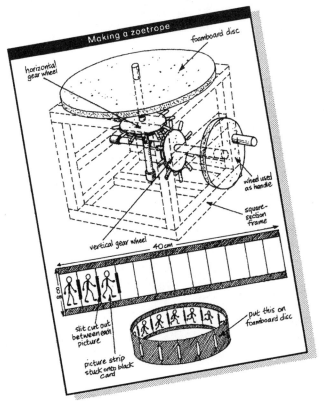

Making a zoetrope

foamboard disc

horizontal gear wheel

wheel used as handle

square-section frame

vertical gear wheel   40 cm

slit cut out between each picture

picture strip stuck onto black card

put this on foamboard disc

**DESIGN AND TECHNOLOGY**

## What to do

Ask the children to look at the pictures of conveyor belts which they have brought in. Talk about how they are used in factories to move items from one process to another. Explain that a moving pavement or walkway is also a type of conveyor belt, although most of the mechanisms are under the ground. Show the children some flexible corrugated cardboard, and demonstrate how this can form the basis of the moving platform. Discuss why this material is effective for the purpose – its corrugations make it strong (see the activity on page 14 in the 'Structures' chapter) but also flexible. The corrugations also make it rough so that it 'sticks' to the pulleys rather than slides over them. There are clearly links with science and work on friction at this point in the activity.

Show the children how to measure the cardboard carefully in a long strip, and how to fasten the ends to produce a continuous belt. Explain that they need two pulleys around which this belt can rotate. One pulley should have a handle on it – this is the *drive* pulley. The other is the *driven* pulley.

Show them the wide range of materials which could be used as pulleys for their conveyor belt. The intention is that this activity gives the children some freedom in identifying ways in which the materials can be used. Photocopiable sheet 125 gives some possible techniques, although the sheet should be used as a reminder after the children have come up with suggestions of their own. Similarly, avoid showing the children the examples of pulleys which you have made until you find their ideas are coming to an end.

Now give out photocopiable sheet 126. This explains the task which is to produce a conveyor belt controlled by a handle and will carry a small chocolate bar a distance of at least 30cm. There is also a generalised drawing on the sheet of what is required . If you set a height for the conveyor belt, say 10cm, this will make it possible for all the groups' conveyor belts to join together for a class display.

Each group should discuss their ideas and come up with initial designs, clearly identifying which of the available materials they wish to use. They should then make and test their conveyor belt.

## Suggestion(s) for extension

These conveyor belts are hand driven, but it would be possible to control them by motors. See the activity 'Making a buggy' (page 86) for the details of incorporating a motor.

## Suggestion(s) for support

This activity gives children an opportunity to select appropriate materials, so the task becomes easier if they have a reduced choice. For groups that are really finding the task difficult, provide an annotated version of photocopiable page 126 showing dimensions and the particular materials which they should select.

## Assessment opportunities

This activity can be used to assess the ability of the children to work co-operatively in groups. It also focuses on children's ability to choose effectively materials and techniques in order to complete a given task.

## Display ideas

If all the conveyor belts are built to the same scale they could be arranged around the classroom and the children could find out how far they can move the chocolate bar.

## Reference to photocopiable sheet

Sheet 125 shows a number of ways in which pulleys can be made and how pulleys and belts can be put together. Sheet 126 sets the task and gives a generalised drawing which the groups can use to form the basis of their design.

**DESIGN AND TECHNOLOGY**

# Energy

This section provides activities which give children an understanding of the widespread use of energy throughout our lives. It focuses upon the use of stored energy, in particular by using elastic bands and balloons, and on alternative sources of energy such as wind and water power. The section concludes with two propeller-powered projects in the form of a boat and a hovercraft. The emphasis in this section is how concepts related to energy can be incorporated into children's practical work. It builds upon work which children will have undertaken in science.

The lesson plans in this chapter aim to develop children's designing skills (discussing ideas, drawing designs, evaluating ideas), and making skills (measuring, cutting, joining, finishing and using appropriate tools and equipment). Some of the later activities require children to undertake considerable evaluative activity if they are to complete the work successfully.

The following contexts are appropriate for work with energy:

▲ alternative sources of energy;
▲ transport;
▲ toys;
▲ games.

# AN ENERGY MAP OF THE SCHOOL

**IDEA**

*To be aware of the different kinds of energy and investigate the types of energy used in school.*

†† *Working in groups of four.*

🕐 *Two one-hour sessions.*

## Previous skills/knowledge needed

An awareness of the different types of energy which they will have covered in their science work.

## Key background information

Energy comes in many forms. By undertaking an energy survey of the school, the extensive use of energy in our lives today can be illustrated. It can also lead on to a discussion of how we can save energy.

## Vocabulary

Heat energy, movement (kinetic) energy, stored (potential) energy, light energy, sound energy, electrical energy.

## Preparation

You will need plans of all areas of the school buildings and grounds. These could have been produced by the children as part of their geography work and should include all of the above types of energy. You will also need to warn staff that small groups of children will be doing research around the school at particular times in the week.

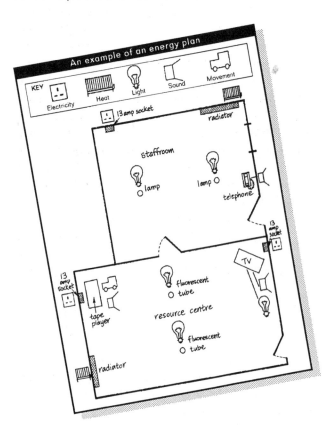

An example of an energy plan

## Resources needed

One copy of photocopiable sheet 127 per group, clipboards, plans of school buildings and grounds, writing materials.

## What to do

Ask the children what they remember of their work on energy in science. Ask them to give examples of different kinds of energy. Write the types of energy on the board. Give each group of children a plan of part of the school building or grounds. Ask the groups to observe carefully at each site, and to mark on their plans all the things that use energy and all the things that provide energy. Either give them a list of appropriate symbols or get the class to devise their own. Photocopiable sheet 127 can be distributed to the groups at this stage as an example of what their own plans will look like.

When the task is completed ask the children to put the data into a database with fields such as *Location, Nature of Device* and *Energy Type*. Graphs and charts could then be produced displaying, for example, the proportion of devices which use *electrical* energy or the locations of all the radiators giving out *heat* energy.

## Suggestion(s) for extension

The children can devise the structure of the database themselves deciding on the field headings. More sophisticated analysis can be done on the data, with the children themselves identifying what should be analysed and how it should be presented.

## Suggestions for support

The groups collecting the data could be of mixed ability. The children could be inputting data into a ready constructed database rather than constructing their own.

## Assessment opportunities

This gives an opportunity to assess children's IT capability in their use of a database. It can also be used to assess how well children can create a map of an area and their ability to design a key.

## Opportunities for IT

The children could use the information they have created to make a database about different energy forms throughout the school. The field names could include the following headings:

| | |
|---|---|
| Location | *hall* |
| Energy type | *heat* |
| Device | *radiator* |
| Input/output | *output* |
| On/off | *on* |
| Energy source | *gas* |

Once the database has been created the children could look for patterns and answer questions such as:

▲ What is the most common form of energy source?

▲ Which area of school uses the most energy?

**DESIGN AND TECHNOLOGY**

The children could also use the graphical facilities of the software to produce graphs showing, for example, the proportion of devices which use electrical energy.

Older pupils may be able to draw a plan of the school using drawing software and indicate the position of the energy sources and users using a simple key. With some mapping packages, such as Aegis 2, it is possible to draw a plan of the school and include the graphical data alongside specific locations on the plan.

### Display ideas
A wall display could be made showing the children's completed plans and analyses of the data collected entitled 'This is where we get our energy from and this is how we use it.' It could also include suggestions as to how savings could be made, for example: 'Do we need all the lights on in the classrooms, or should we make sure they are switched off when there is no one in the room?'

### Reference to photocopiable sheet
Sheet 127 provides an example of an energy plan.

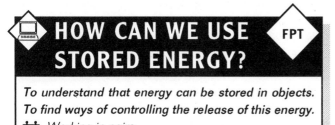

## HOW CAN WE USE STORED ENERGY? FPT

*To understand that energy can be stored in objects.*
*To find ways of controlling the release of this energy.*
†† *Working in pairs.*
🕐 *Two one-hour sessions.*
⚠ *Be aware of the dangers of elastic bands and balloons being flicked around the room and into children's eyes.*

### Previous skills/knowledge needed
An understanding of stored energy in the form of a stretched elastic band.

### Key background information
A stretched elastic band stores energy. When it is released it moves very quickly through the air – the *stored* energy being transferred into *movement* energy. (This could be a demonstration rather than a class activity!) A blown-up balloon also is able to store energy in its elasticity.

### Vocabulary
Stored (or potential) energy.

### Preparation
Make a small 'test bed' from a construction kit to demonstrate the way in which the wheels can be made to rotate. You also need to build a small buggy from the construction kit for children who need support.

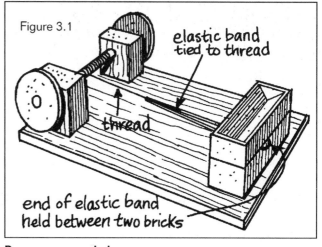

Figure 3.1

elastic band tied to thread

thread

end of elastic band held between two bricks

### Resources needed
A variety of elastic bands, balloons, construction kit with wheels and axles (you will need sufficient for each pair to be able to build a simple four-wheeled buggy), timing and measuring device.

### What to do
Remind children that energy can be stored in springs and elastic bands. Show them a simple wheel and axle made out of a construction kit. Tie one end of a piece of thread to the axle, and the other end to the elastic band. Wind the thread around the axle. Now stretch the elastic band and fix it to another part of the structure. Release it and watch the wheel and axle spin round.

Tell the children they are going to make a device which works on this principle (see Figure 3.1). Using a construction kit they should build a small buggy. An elastic band should be tied to a piece of thread. The thread is wound tightly round the axle and the elastic band is fixed at the far end of the buggy while the axle is held steady. Now release the wheel and axle and watch as the elastic band gradually returns to its original length, unwinding the thread as it goes resulting in the wheels turning. The children can be asked to try different elastic bands and different sizes of wheel to see which set-up can make the buggy travel for the longest time. Each group could then use their model in a trial. Tests can be carried out to see which vehicle travels the fastest and which vehicle travels the greatest distance.

Demonstrate how a balloon is elastic and how its stored energy (when inflated) can be changed into movement energy (when it is released). This motion is far from controlled, but it could be harnessed. Again, using a small buggy, ask the children to investigate how they can move their vehicles using 'balloon power' (see Figure 3.2). They should consider the lightness of the buggy and the speed with which the air comes out. If it comes out too quickly, the buggy does not have time to overcome its inertia and start moving; if it comes out too slowly, there is insufficient force to move it. Putting the end of the balloon through one of the holes in a construction kit brick can give a satisfactory rate of flow.

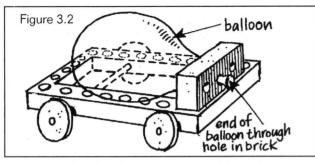

Figure 3.2

Again, speed and or distance trials could be undertaken. In both activities, results could be recorded in a database, and graphs and charts produced summarising the results of the class (see Figure 3.3).

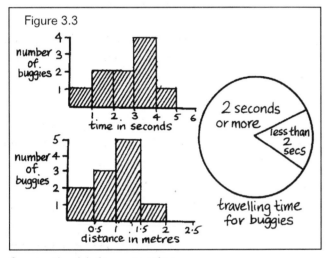

Figure 3.3

### Suggestion(s) for extension
This basic principle can be utilised in models made out of wood, plastic, foamboard, card and so on. Wooden buggies could be constructed, and they could be made to move using either elastic bands or balloons.

### Suggestion(s) for support
Show the children how to make the small buggy or give them the sample buggy which you made so that they can focus on the way in which the energy from the elastic band and balloon have a controlled release.

### Assessment opportunities
This activity requires children to solve problems as a member of a group. They also need to be able to identify criteria which need to be considered, such as the lightness of the vehicle and the speed at which the air is released.

### Opportunities for IT
The children could use a spreadsheet to record the results of their tests. A class spreadsheet could be set up with a row for each pair of children. The spreadsheet could also be set up to include formula to work out speed from the distance and time measurements, or to work out averages from a number of tests using the same type of vehicle. The spreadsheets might look like the following examples:

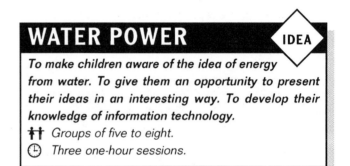

|   | a | b | c | d |
|---|---|---|---|---|
| 1 | Name | distance | time | speed |
| 2 | John & Inderjit | 50 | 2.4 | b2/c2 |
| 3 | Sarah & Jenny | 150 | 3.2 | b3/c3 |
|   |   |   |   |   |

|   | a | b | c | d | e |
|---|---|---|---|---|---|
| 1 | Name | try 1 | try 2 | try 3 | average |
| 2 | John & Inderjit | 50 | 75 | 120 | sum(b2:d2)/3 |
| 3 | Sarah & Jenny | 150 | 166 | 200 | sum(b3:d3)/3 |
|   |   |   |   |   |   |

The results of individual tests could be analysed against the class's results using the graphical and statistical functions.

### Display ideas
Each of the models can be retained for display and the results of the time and speed trial can be displayed as well.

## WATER POWER — IDEA

*To make children aware of the idea of energy from water. To give them an opportunity to present their ideas in an interesting way. To develop their knowledge of information technology.*

†† *Groups of five to eight.*

🕐 *Three one-hour sessions.*

### Previous skills/knowledge needed
Children should be familiar with the basic idea that moving water can be used to turn wheels. This turning of wheels can subsequently be transformed into other mechanical movement. Ideally some work on energy will have already been undertaken in science.

### Key background information
Water power has been used for thousands of years and it comes in many different forms. If water is required to move heavy machinery it needs to flow quite slowly, but if it is used to produce electricity it needs to flow very quickly.

### Vocabulary
Turbine, hydroelectricity.

### Preparation
You will need to have a large amount of background material for this topic. This should include posters, videos, photographic slides and CD-ROM material. This can be obtained from a wide range of organisations. The children will also need access to hardware in the form of computers, printers and perhaps an overhead projector for presenting their ideas. This is an opportunity for children to use any Internet link which the school may have.

## Resources needed

Computers, printers, overhead projector, slide projector, reference material (as suggested above) and copies of photocopiable sheets 128 and 129 for each child.

## What to do

Introduce the idea that flowing water can be used as a source of energy. Use some of the resource materials to give both an interesting start to the activity and an opportunity to show how the children can present their ideas. Give each child a copy of photocopiable sheet 128 which gives some illustrations of four ways in which water is used as a source of energy. Split the class into four groups and allocate one of the methods to each group. (If you have a very large class it would probably be better to have eight groups with each use of water being researched by two of them.)

Each group should now be given copies of photocopiable sheet 129 which outlines the structure of a presentation which each group should make to the rest of the class (or other classes in the school). In approximately five to ten minutes, they need to put over the main ideas of how water can be or has been used to obtain energy.

Ask each group to nominate a leader who should co-ordinate the work of the group. Leave them to contemplate the resource materials and give them access to computers and printers so that they can produce handouts or overhead transparencies for their presentations. It may be necessary to provide 'training' sessions in the use of some of this equipment if they are not familiar with it. This activity can also provide a reason for learning to use the IT based equipment.

It is important to give adequate time for the presentations to be prepared if they are to be of a high quality. Encourage all group members to contribute to the actual presentation. Also try to avoid gender stereotypical roles within the presentation.

During the presentations children should make notes so that they have a record of all four methods of obtaining energy from water, but a detailed knowledge of one of them.

## Suggestion(s) for extension

If children have access to extensive IT facilities they could be asked to make use of this in their presentations. They could desktop publish a handout or use a presentation program to produce overhead transparencies. It would also be possible to make a multi-media presentation on their topic if the school has access to such software (see 'Opportunities for IT').

## Suggestion(s) for support

One of the most difficult aspects of this project for some children will be an effective sharing out of the tasks within the group. The teacher actually nominating each child to undertake a task will limit the degree of autonomy within the group, but for some children this may be appropriate.

If children are having difficulty grasping how water moves equipment, provide a model of a water-wheel.

## Assessment opportunities

This activity gives a good opportunity to evaluate children's ability to work as a member of a team. The work they do can be used to assess how good their understanding of water as a means to produce energy is. It also provides assessment of the children's advanced IT skills.

## Opportunities for IT

The children could use a CD-ROM to research information about different forms of water power and how it is used. They could go on to use this information within a word processor or desktop publishing package to present their information to the class, either in a printed form, or as a spoken presentation. Alternatively, use multi-media authoring software to create an electronic presentation to be produced by a single group, or by the class pooling its information with each group being responsible for one part of the presentation. (See 'Wind energy' on page 41.)

## Display ideas

This activity will produce a great deal of visual information which can easily be mounted to form a wall display illustrating the different types of water power.

## Reference to photocopiable sheets

Sheet 128 gives some limited details about the four main ways of obtaining power from flowing water. Sheet 129 provides one way of structuring the children's presentations. The tasks are for guidance only, and extra ones could be added and/or some removed.

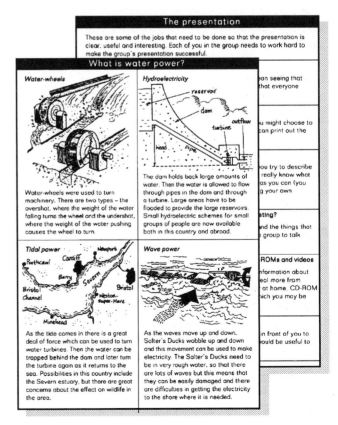

## GETTING WATER TO DO WORK

**FPT**

*To build a simple water-wheel that will lift a small load. To extend the children's accuracy of cutting. To gain an understanding of evaluation criteria.*

†† *Working in pairs.*

◷ *Two one-hour sessions.*

⚠ *Care must be taken when cutting the plastic lemonade bottle using a craft knife and should be done under close supervision.*

### Previous skills/knowledge needed

Children will need an understanding of how water-wheels work. They should have undertaken the activity 'Water power' on page 38, or something similar, to gain the understanding that energy can be harnessed from water.

### Key background information

There are problems making water do useful work in a classroom model. Although a water turbine can be connected to a motor (used as a generator), the quantity of electricity produced is very small. This may show up on a voltmeter, but it is insufficient to do much that is very useful. Similarly, although water can turn a water-wheel, there is generally little turning force, so that it cannot be transmitted by a mechanism to make anything move. This activity just allows children to see that water can be used to produce movement energy in a relatively unrealistic situation. However, the pressure in a mains tap can be quite substantial with surprising results.

### Vocabulary

Evaluation, criteria.

### Preparation

You will need to have produced one of the large plastic container turbines to see how it works and the problems that might be encountered. You will also need a selection of turbines made up using a range of different materials (see photocopiable sheet 130).

### Resources needed

Large plastic containers, junk materials (see photocopiable sheet 130), dowel, corrugated plastic, plastic spoons, corks, craft knives, paper drill, small loads to be lifted, string, metre rule, measuring jug, scales, prepared large turbines and other turbines, one copy of photocopiable sheet 130 per pair.

### What to do

Remind the children of the work they have done on water power. Tell them that they are now going to make a water-wheel which will turn round and wind up a load. Arrange the children in pairs and give each pair photocopiable sheet 130. Tell them that they will build the basic structure in a large plastic container. Show them the other materials out of which they might make the water-wheel.

Ask them to think about the following questions:

▲ How are you going to provide water for the turbine – from a tap or through a plastic tube?

▲ Is it necessary for all the materials to be waterproof?

▲ Could you use sticky-backed plastic to waterproof it?

▲ Does the whole model need to be in a waterproof tray?

▲ What sort of adhesive will you need to use if the material is going to get wet?

Now ask the pairs to build and test their water-wheels. This activity could be extended into a competition with a whole range of different criteria. The one which, for example:

▲ lifts the load furthest with one litre of water;

▲ lifts the heaviest load with one litre of water;

▲ creates the least mess!

### Suggestion(s) for extension

The water-wheel could be incorporated into a building like a mill used to grind flour. The same principles would apply, but more time would be necessary to produce an aesthetically pleasing product.

### Suggestions for support

Children can be supported by guiding them into using particular materials for the construction of the water-wheel, rather than giving them choice.

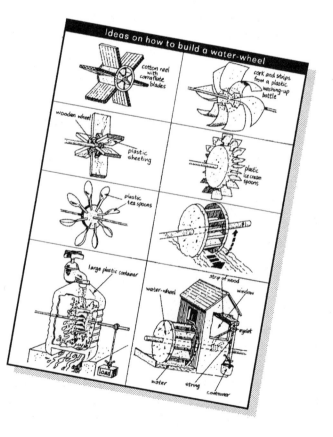

**DESIGN AND TECHNOLOGY**

### Assessment opportunities

This activity could be used to focus upon the accuracy of cutting (for example, a neat shape out of the plastic container, and the accuracy of the water-wheel turbine) and to measure children's ability to understand criteria for evaluation.

### Opportunities for IT

The children could use a drawing or CAD (computer aided design) package to draw the design for their water-wheel. They could also use a word processor to write and print labels to go with their models for the class display.

### Display ideas

Display the models with labels emphasising their positive features, for example: 'This model was very stable because it was filled with stones and pebbles'.

### Reference to photocopiable sheet

Sheet 130 shows how to build a simple water-wheel turbine, showing possible methods and materials.

---

## WIND ENERGY
**IDEA**

*To develop an awareness of how the wind provides us with energy.*

**††** *Whole class working individually.*

🕐 *1 hour.*

### Previous skills/knowledge needed

Children should have undertaken work on energy in their science lessons.

### Key background information

This activity gives some basic facts about energy from the wind. In particular, it focuses on features which they should consider when building their own wind-powered models.

### Vocabulary

Wind turbine, source of energy, blade.

### Resources needed

Reference books, photographs, posters, videos and CD-ROMs illustrating aspects of wind energy (windmills, wind turbines), photocopiable sheets 131, 132 and 133, one per child, extra paper if necessary.

### What to do

Show children the pictures of windmills and wind turbines. Ask them what they are and what they are used for. Ask why windmills have blades and why they are a particular shape. The discussion should lead to an understanding that they both use the wind as a source of energy, but that one is used to move machinery and the other is used to provide electricity.

Give the children photocopiable sheets 131, 132 and 133. Depending on the reading ability of the class, either let the children read the sheets individually, and then answer the questions, or discuss the work and talk through the questions as a whole class before the children write down their answers.

### Suggestion(s) for extension

Instead of asking the children to write down the answers to the questions they should devise a game incorporating questions and answers on wind power. Once this is done individually, they can try out their games in pair or groups of four. The questions could be limited to the material covered in this activity, or you could allow the children to do further research using a library or CD-ROM in order to make the game more interesting.

### Suggestion(s) for support

You could highlight sections of the information sheet to identify the location the children should be looking in. Let the children join in the games produced by other groups before writing the answers to the questions. They could work in pairs, one supporting the other.

### Assessment opportunities

This activity provides the opportunity to assess how well children understand the idea of using wind as a source of energy and, from the extension activity, how well they are able to obtain specific information from a range of sources.

### Opportunities for IT

The children can use a CD-ROM encyclopaedia to research information on wind energy. The children could go on to use a word processor or a desktop publishing package to present the information that they have found. Individual groups of children could research one particular feature and present this information. A class book or display could be made from the resulting work.

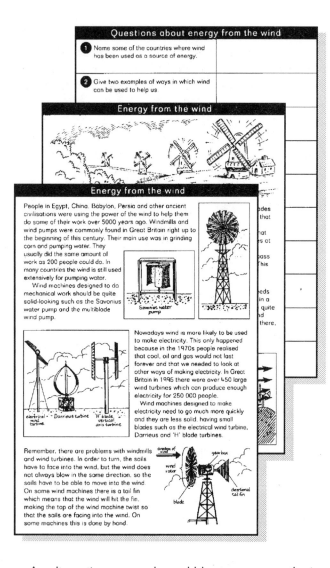

**Questions about energy from the wind**

1. Name some of the countries where wind has been used as a source of energy.

2. Give two examples of ways in which wind can be used to help us.

**Energy from the wind**

**Energy from the wind**

People in Egypt, China, Babylon, Persia and other ancient civilisations were using the power of the wind to help them do some of their work over 5000 years ago. Windmills and wind pumps were commonly found in Great Britain right up to the beginning of this century. Their main use was in grinding corn and pumping water. They usually did the same amount of work as 200 people could do. In many countries the wind is still used extensively for pumping water.

Wind machines designed to do mechanical work should be quite solid-looking such as the Savonius water pump and the multiblade wind pump.

Nowadays wind is more likely to be used to make electricity. This only happened because in the 1970s people realised that coal, oil and gas would not last forever and that we needed to look at other ways of making electricity. In Great Britain in 1995 there were over 450 large wind turbines which can produce enough electricity for 250 000 people.

Wind machines designed to make electricity need to go much more quickly and they are less solid, having small blades such as the electrical wind turbine, Darrieus and 'H' blade turbines.

Remember, there are problems with windmills and wind turbines. In order to turn, the sails have to face into the wind, but the wind does not always blow in the same direction, so the sails have to be able to move into the wind. On some wind machines there is a tail fin which means that the wind will hit the fin, making the top of the wind machine twist so that the sails are facing into the wind. On some machines this is done by hand.

---

An alternative approach would be to use an authoring package to create a multi-media presentation. The groups could search and present information on a particular use of wind power. They could include pictures taken from clip art, CD-ROM collections or their own line drawings. Children could even add their own voices, recorded using a microphone linked to the computer. The initial structure could be set up in advance with a front page showing a list of the different forms of wind power, so that by clicking on one form, the user would be taken to a page showing all the information about that source. This is a fairly ambitious project and children using the software for the first time will need help and support.

### Display ideas

Selected children should put their answers to particular questions onto a large sheet of paper, and these should be incorporated into a display on 'Energy from the wind'.

### Reference to photocopiable sheets

Sheets 131 and 132 give information about making energy from the wind. Sheet 133 provides questions which can be answered by reference to the other sheets, but which could be dealt with more fully if further research was undertaken.

---

# TRAVELLING TOWARDS THE WIND
### FPT

*To make a wind-powered vehicle. To make use of their knowledge about the use of pulleys. To understand the importance of evaluation throughout the whole of an activity.*

†† *Working in groups of five.*

🕐 *Four one-hour sessions.*

⚠ *Use a metal safety rule and cutting mat when using a craft knife. Take care when using a saw.*

### Previous skills/knowledge needed

Children should have done work using pulleys. In particular, they should be familiar with the idea that a crossed-over belt can change the direction of pulley wheels, and that a fast rotation can be turned into a slow and more powerful rotation using a small pulley on one axle and a large one on the other (see diagram below).

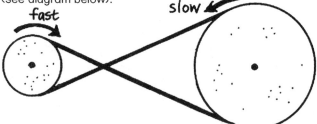

They should have talked about the use of wind power, and discussed the shape of suitable wind turbine blades (see photocopiable sheets 131 and 132). It will be useful if children have already completed the 'Wind energy' activity on page 41.

### Key background information

The children need to be familiar with the concept of two pulleys linked together with a crossed-over drive belt. Then, when the wind turbine is made to turn by the wind (or a hair-dryer), the twisted belt turns the axle in the opposite direction, causing the vehicle to move towards the wind. This is not a particularly realistic situation, but it does allow children to engage in an interesting problem-solving activity.

### Vocabulary

Wind turbine, evaluation, prototype.

### Preparation

Decide on the exact quantities and types of materials that you will make available to the children. This is important, because if you do not specify this, the activity can be very expensive in terms of resources. Cutting sheet material into reasonable sized pieces (20cm by 30cm) rather than providing large pieces of material, will focus the children's minds on the activity. Photocopiable sheet 134 provides children with one possible solution if they are having difficulty. It should not be handed out to groups at the beginning of the activity.

**DESIGN AND TECHNOLOGY**

## Resources needed

Corrugated plastic sheet, foamboard, dowel, square-section wood, PVA adhesive, clear solvent-free adhesive, cotton reels, cardboard, wooden wheels, large and small pulleys, elastic bands, photocopiable sheet 134 if required.

## What to do

Remind the children of the work they have done on wind generators (for example 'Wind energy' on page 41). Concentrate particularly on the ways in which wind can be 'caught' in order to make something spin round. Then set the problem.

Ask the children to work in groups of five to design a vehicle that will actually travel towards the source of the wind rather than away from it. Show them the hair-dryer, and the 'wind power' which it is able to provide. Show children the range of materials which are available to them. You might decide to let children use other materials which they bring in from home, but a functioning model can be made with the material identified above.

Groups should be encouraged to sketch out their ideas, experiment with the materials, and produce prototypes of their vehicle. The hair-dryer should be available so that children can try out their ideas as they are going along. Children should be reminded of the role of evaluation throughout the activity. An important role of the teacher is to offer both support and challenge to the groups as they work.

When all the models are complete, you should arrange a final presentation session. Discuss which are the best models with the children and then help them to identify that there need to be criteria in order to evaluate effectively. In this case the criteria could be:

▲ the fastest;
▲ the most streamlined;
▲ the one that used the fewest resources;
▲ the most aesthetically pleasing and so on.

## Suggestion(s) for extension

In its existing form, the focus is purely on getting the models to function as required. Children could be asked to ensure that their models looked good and were suitably decorated to fit in with a theme of their choice.

## Suggestion(s) for support

The most difficult part of this activity is understanding the need for a pulley system (a) with a small pulley on the wind generator and a large pulley on the drive axle and (b) with a crossed-over drive belt to cause the wheels to move in the opposite direction to the wind generator.

It is with these ideas that some children may need extra support, to the extent, in some cases, of being told where the pulleys should go and the need for a crossed-over drive belt. Photocopiable sheet 134 could be made available to those children who are having problems with the activity.

## Assessment opportunities

This activity gives many opportunities for assessing the effectiveness of group work, children's skills in evaluating and also the ability of children to select from their past experiences in order to solve problems. For this reason it must be noted that if the children are instructed on how to use the pulleys and the drive belt in order to make the model work, the nature of the activity changes radically, and thus some of the assessment opportunities disappear.

## Opportunities for IT

The children could use a word processor to write an evaluation of the model they have made. This could be printed out in the form of a label to go next to the model in the class display. Children could also use a drawing or CAD package to make annotated drawings of their design.

## Display ideas

A collection of the finished models could be put on display. Under the heading 'Evaluation Criterion' a label should be attached to each model on which is a criterion which could have made it the best:

▲ the cheapest;
▲ the fastest;
▲ the one which was built in the shortest time.

## Reference to photocopiable sheet

Sheet 134 contains one possible design of vehicle and should be used as support material only.

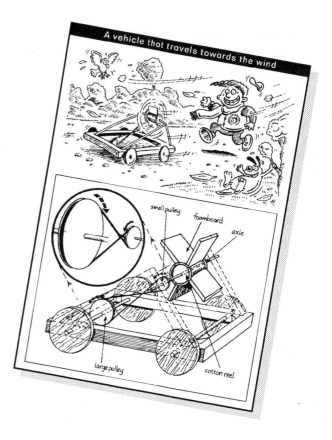

**DESIGN AND TECHNOLOGY**

# A PROPELLER-POWERED BOAT

**FPT**

*To design and make a propeller-powered boat. To overcome problems encountered during the activity. To evaluate the children's work throughout the designing and making of the boat.*

†† *Working in pairs.*

⏰ *Three one-hour sessions.*

⚠ *Use a metal safety rule and cutting board when using a craft knife. Take care when using a saw.*

## Previous skills/knowledge needed
Children should already have done some work in science on floating and sinking, and stability. They should also have done some simple circuit work, probably using a motor.

## Key background information
The propeller on this boat provides thrust through the air. This is how the boats work in the Everglades in Florida. Great care needs to be taken in the location of the propeller, motor, and battery, to ensure that the boat remains stable. This activity gives opportunities for the children to look at the waterproof properties of materials and also at stability.

## Vocabulary
Propeller, stability, prototype, evaluation.

## Preparation
You need a three-metre long length of plastic guttering, sealed at both ends, and filled with water to provide your 'testing tank'. You will also need samples of materials which the children could use for their boats.

## Resources needed
Plastic guttering 'tank', corraflute, glue gun adhesive, square-section wood, plastic containers, battery, battery holders, battery clip, switch, propeller, motor, motor holder, wire, solder, soldering iron, waterproof sealant, craft knife, metal safety rule, cutting mat, saw, bench hook, G-cramp, timer, copies of photocopiable sheet 135 for children who need support.

## What to do
Show children the piece of sealed plastic guttering in which you will test the finished boats. Ideally, it should be full of water, so that the children can visualise the possible depth of the boat as well as its other dimensions. Discuss the types of materials which could be used, for example: corraflute being plastic would form a waterproof base, but excellent seals are needed to ensure water does not leak in causing the boat to sink.

Talk about the basic requirements of the activity:
▲ the boat needs a base, which needs to be waterproof;
▲ it needs sides to stop water from entering the boat;
▲ it needs a shape which will make it move through the water easily;
▲ it needs a holder for the motor and a propeller blade, which must be high enough to prevent the propeller from hitting the sides of the boat or the water, but not so high that the boat will become unstable and topple over.

And where should the motor be positioned? If it is too near the back or the front then the boat again becomes unstable. But if it is centrally placed, the battery has to go either at the back or the front, and this again may cause instability.

Discuss waterproof glues, and ways to seal any gaps in the boat. As the aim is to build the fastest boat, the children also need to consider issues relating to its lightness, and the size of the battery, motor and propeller, although it would probably be wise to keep these last three elements the same in each of the models. The children should now make their models and test them.

## Suggestion(s) for extension
The same activity can be undertaken, but with far less advance discussion of the important features. More able and experienced children will then find out the problems for themselves and will need to devise strategies to overcome them. Without the support and suggested design, the activity is far more open-ended, and could easily become a design and make activity (DMA), as it provides many opportunities for choice.

## Suggestion(s) for support
Photocopiable sheet 135 gives a limited range of suggestions, with some warnings about what to watch out for in the design. This would be suitable for some of the less able children in a group or for all children in a group who were inexperienced in doing this sort of work.

**DESIGN AND TECHNOLOGY**

## Assessment opportunities

This activity gives opportunities to see how children can work together to solve problems. Prototyping and evaluation will be much in evidence during this activity. They should be evaluating, in particular, the use of appropriate raw materials, the waterproofing and the speed of the completed craft.

## Opportunities for IT

The children could use a word processor to write an evaluation of the model boat they have made. This could be printed out in the form of a label to go next to the model in the class display. Children could also use a drawing or CAD package to make annotated drawings of their design.

They could also use a spreadsheet to record the results of the tests. The spreadsheet could be used to automatically work out the speed of the boats through the water. The spreadsheet might look something like this:

|   | a | b | c | d |
|---|---|---|---|---|
| 1 | Name | distance | time | speed |
| 2 | David and Balpinder | 200 | 2.4 | b2/c2 |
| 3 | Kate & Greg | 200 | 3.2 | b3/c3 |
|   |   |   |   |   |

A more ambitious project would be to set up an electronic timer linked to the computer. This would use a sensor to detect when the boat passes the start mark and another sensor to detect when it crosses the finish mark. The software would then automatically work out the time between the two points. The switches could be simple contact switches or infrared beams.

## Display ideas

The testing of the boats on the water channel could be done in front of a larger audience, of adults, for example, at a parents' evening, or of children at an assembly. The different boats could be on display together with the times logged of the first three craft. The models could have threads attached to features which made these boats go quicker than the others, and word-processed explanations could be on the wall attached to the other end of the thread.

## Reference to photocopiable sheet

Support sheet 135 shows some of the important features that need to be considered as the boat is being designed.

## A HOVERCRAFT    FPT

*To design and make a hovercraft and to understand the basic principles of how it works.*

†† *Working in pairs.*

🕐 *Three one-hour sessions.*

⚠ *Use of a metal safety rule and a cutting board when using a craft knife and a compass cutter. Take care when using a saw.*

## Previous skills/knowledge needed

Children should have built models with electric motors.

## Key background information

A hovercraft works by pushing down air towards the ground which creates a blanket of air on which the craft floats. It is difficult to create sufficient pressure to lift things off the ground, so it is vital that the hovercraft is light. Designing a light hovercraft is an important feature of this activity. Hovercraft were invented in Britain by Christopher Cockerell.

## Vocabulary

Hovercraft, lift, skirt.

## Preparation

You need to find pictures and videos of hovercraft in action (including small ones which use motor cycle engines and those which take cars and passengers across the English Channel every day). You also need supplies of the materials which are recommended for this activity so that they can be shown during the introductory session together with one completed model which works effectively.

## Resources needed

Pictures of hovercraft, a video clip of a hovercraft in action (if possible), polystyrene sheet, balloons, thin cardboard, motor, motor holder, small propeller, battery, battery holder, compass cutter, non-solvent based clear adhesive, one copy of photocopiable sheet 136 per child.

## What to do

Introduce the lesson by showing children a fan and how air is pushed away from the fan blades. Let them stand in front of the fan to feel the air. Show them pictures and videos of hovercraft. Ask them what they think the advantages of hovercraft are. Tell children how important it is to make the hovercraft very light. Ask them to suggest materials which they could use. Polystyrene foam sheet is a suitable material. You can then demonstrate the basic feature of the hovercraft by blowing up a balloon and fixing the end into a small hole in the centre of a small sheet of polystyrene foam. As the air escapes from the balloon, the foam rises slightly from the table.

How can we improve upon this?

▲ First discuss how you can keep the air from escaping too quickly. Remind them of the skirt on the real hovercraft they have seen. How can you provide a much longer-lasting supply of air? A motor with a propeller will provide this air, and some sort of tunnel is needed to make sure all the air goes in the right direction.

How will the motor be powered?

▲ Batteries would seem to be the most appropriate solution, but they are often relatively heavy, and this might make it impossible for the hovercraft to lift. One solution would be to keep the batteries off the model and to have long leads leading from the hovercraft to the batteries.

Now let the children see photocopiable sheet 136 which illustrates some possible approaches to constructing this model. It is not a step-by-step instruction sheet, so it leaves the children to make some design decisions. Show them the resources that are available. Remind them how to use a compass cutter, and the use of non-solvent based clear adhesive for sticking cardboard to polystyrene, emphasising

the correct use, that is, leaving both surfaces to become tacky before joining firmly together. They also need to bear in mind the size of the propeller and the way in which the motor will be held firmly in place, ensuring that the hovercraft does not become too heavy. The way in which the motor is fixed in place should be left to each group to decide.

### Suggestion(s) for extension

The way in which the hovercraft is designed means that it will lift off the ground, but will not move forward. Children could be asked to devise ways of making it move forward. This can be done either by adding an additional motor and propeller at right angles to the original, or by diverting some of the air flow from the existing motor.

Neither idea is without its problems. By adding an extra motor, you are increasing the weight considerably, and you may not have sufficient lift. By diverting some of the existing air flow to provide forward thrust, you are not having as much downward thrust, which means that it may not continue to lift off the floor.

To complete this extension activity satisfactorily the children will need to have had extensive experience in designing and making, and have considerable patience. It will also be very time consuming so it is probably more suitable for a 'Technology Club' activity.

### Suggestion(s) for support

Those children who are having difficulties with this activity would benefit from seeing the sample model which you have produced. The main problems children will encounter are making the hovercraft sufficiently light, and fixing the motor in place. If the children are able to see how these problems are overcome in a fully working model, then they are more likely to succeed.

### Assessment opportunities

Children who complete this activity successfully will have shown considerable determination as well as effective making and problem-solving skills. They will also be able to work quite independently.

### Opportunities for IT

Children could use a word processor or desktop publishing package to write an evaluation, highlighting the strengths and weaknesses of each model as already identified. These could be displayed next to the models.

### Display ideas

The hovercraft could be displayed, and next to each model should be a desktop-published sheet as in 'Opportunities for IT' above.

### Reference to photocopiable sheet

Sheet 136 shows one basic design for a simple hovercraft.

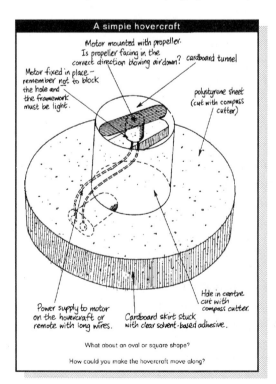

A simple hovercraft

Motor mounted with propeller.
Is propeller facing in the correct direction blowing air down? cardboard tunnel

Motor fixed in place – remember not to block the hole and the framework must be light.

polystyrene sheet (cut with compass cutter)

Power supply to motor on the hovercraft or remote with long wires.

Cardboard skirt stuck with clear solvent-based adhesive.

Hole in centre cut with compass cutter.

What about an oval or square shape?

How could you make the hovercraft move along?

DESIGN AND
TECHNOLOGY

# Mouldable materials

This section provides a range of focused practical tasks using a wide range of materials which can be moulded. Each activity focuses upon the skills and techniques which should be learned in order to work effectively with the medium, and is set in a context which will allow children to practise and develop the techniques they learn. It is important to realise that these materials will come in useful in many other projects, and that children should be reminded of their particular properties whenever they are working on a design and make activity, when they could choose to use some of these materials.

The actual activities and the modelling materials used could easily be interchanged to fit into your scheme of work more effectively. Masks could be made from papier mâché, and jewellery from salt dough, for example. What is more important is that children experience working with a wide range of media, and that they are aware of the strengths and weaknesses of each so that they can make informed decisions when they need to select appropriate materials for design and make activities.

Most of the activity sheets associated with these activities provide a summary of the techniques which children need to know in order to work with these materials effectively. As such, they form a useful reference source, to assist children when undertaking design and make tasks where they need to select materials.

**DESIGN AND TECHNOLOGY**

## MUSICAL MARACAS  ◆ FPT

*To develop skills and techniques related to working with papier mâché. To work co-operatively on a task.*

†† *Working in pairs.*

🕐 *Two one-hour sessions.*

⚠ *The wallpaper paste used should not have a fungicide in it. This is because some children can have allergic reactions to the chemical fungicide. Remind children that they should not put small items in their mouths, such as beads or dried pulses, due to the dangers of choking if they are swallowed. Nuts should not be used. Take care when using the craft knife to cut the papier mâché shell. This should be done under close adult supervision.*

### Previous skills/knowledge needed

Children will need to have done scientific investigations on using shakers to make sounds. They will be aware of the sort of noise which beads or dried pulses make when shaken in a container.

### Key background information

This activity is a good opportunity to highlight some of the important differences between science, and design and technology. A typical science activity would involve putting some beads into a yoghurt pot, sealing the lid and using it as a shaker illustrating how the sound is formed. There is no consideration given to the look of the product or how well it would stand up to extensive use, because the focus of the scientific activity is on investigation. In design and technology, the way in which the sound is made is not the only criterion, and that is where the focus of this activity is to be found – in making a quality pair of maracas.

### Vocabulary

Papier mâché, pulses, maracas, sistrum, sekere, angklung.

### Preparation

Ideally you should have available a selection of shakers from different times and from other cultures (see above).

### Resources needed

Newspaper, wallpaper paste (without fungicide), acrylic paint, acrylic varnish, dowel, dried pulses, beads, PVA adhesive, saw, G-cramp, bench hook, paintbrush, craft knife, cutting mat, copies of photocopiable sheet 137 for each pair.

### What to do

Show children some examples of percussion instruments that involve shaking. Particular ones to focus upon include the maracas from Brazil and Cuba; the sistrum, a U-shaped rattle used in ancient Egypt, Greece and Italy and now often used in Ethiopian religious music; the sekere from Nigeria and the angklung from Indonesia (all of which are to be found on Microsoft's Musical instruments CD-ROM).

Place the children in pairs and hand out photocopiable sheet 137. Go through the basic techniques of how to make a pair of maracas with the children using the sheet as a visual reference. Explain some of the choices which they can make.

▲ The basic shape of the maracas can be formed by a balloon or a large lump of Plasticine. Put a layer of dampened tissue paper over the mould so that the papier mâché will not stick to it. Then add another five or six layers of small squares of newspaper using wallpaper paste as the adhesive. Allow this to dry – putting it near a radiator overnight may speed up the process. Then the children should cut the shell horizontally into two pieces, using a craft knife. Carefully remove the Plasticine or the rubber from the burst balloon.

▲ The next part requires considerable care. One end of the dowel needs to be stuck inside the top part of the papier mâché shell. Use PVA adhesive and let it dry before you touch it again. A small hole needs to be made at the centre of the lower part of the shell for the other end of the dowel to pass through. Add the pulses or beads inside the top of the shell, and slide the lower part over the dowel handle until it once again makes a complete shell. Use masking tape to temporarily keep the two halves in place. Using more torn-up newspaper and wallpaper paste, join the two halves together again, and join the wooden handle to the base of the shell, providing a strong joint.

▲ At this stage, the maracas should actually work, but make sure the children let them dry before they experiment with them too much. (They will not sound very good if the papier mâché shell is still wet.) The children are then free to decorate the maracas with paint, varnish and perhaps a few beads. They should be reminded that each of a *pair* of maracas should look very similar! Emphasise the importance of finishing and the quality of the finished product. The children can now rehearse their class maracas ensemble!

**DESIGN AND TECHNOLOGY**

# Mouldable materials

Making some maracas

balloon or lump of Plasticine

damped tissue paper first, followed by newspaper squares and wallpaper paste — (paper mâché)

cut the shell in half horizontally using a craft knife

dowel stuck to top using PVA adhesive – do not move until dry

do not forget that the dried pulses in now!

hole made in bottom of shell for dowel to go through

keep the two sides together with masking tape

then add more papier mâché to the join and to the handle

when it is dry paint it, add decorations and varnish

often a good idea to limit the number of words that they are allowed so that they have to look carefully at the text to decide which is the most important information; they should also be shown how to use the word count facility of the word processor to assist with this task. Pictures can be included which may be taken from the CD-ROM, drawn using a drawing or art package or scanned from the children's own line drawings.

A more ambitious approach would be to create an electronic presentation about different maracas using a multi-media authoring package. The teacher could set up the structure in advance with a title page that consisted of a list of the different maracas. Children could work in pairs to design two or three linked pages about a particular instrument containing text and pictures taken from CD-ROMs, scanned from their own drawings or drawn using an art package. The sounds of the different maracas could be added either by using sound clips taken from a CD-ROM or by recording them using a microphone attached to the computer.

### Display idea
A performance for another class or at an assembly using the musical instruments.

### Reference to photocopiable sheet
Sheet 137 gives an exploded annotated diagram indicating a possible procedure for making maracas. The children can use it as a visual reference to help them make their instruments.

### Suggestion(s) for extension
Some children may not be happy with the overall sound they are achieving and they could investigate what happens when changes to the 'filling' are made, and if the shell is much thicker. A wide range of other instruments could be manufactured using similar techniques including other percussion and stringed instruments.

### Suggestion(s) for support
Extra adult assistance may be required when the shell is being cut and reconstructed with the handle. Try to avoid doing it for them by offering limited assistance.

### Assessment opportunities
Have the children an understanding of quality products, which function well and also look good? How well were they able to discuss problems within the pair? This can be measured to an extent by how similar the two maracas are. A good pair of children might have decided to work on the maracas together, rather than doing one each.

### Opportunities for IT
The children could use a CD-ROM encyclopaedia such as Microsoft's 'Musical Instruments' to research pictures and information on different sorts of shakers.

Children could extend the activity by using the above information to word process a short account of one particular instrument. This could form part of a class display, or children's individual work bound to make a class book. The children should be shown how to save the text from the CD-ROM in ASCII format and load this into their word processor for editing. It is

## GENUINE JEWELLERY ◁ FPT

*To develop skills and techniques related to working with Formello or Fimo modelling medium.*
*To design and make a piece of jewellery of their own choice, using these techniques.*

†† *Working individually.*
🕐 *Two one-hour sessions.*
⚠ *Use oven gloves when placing into or removing baking trays from the oven. Allow the products to cool before attempting to remove them from the aluminium foil. Make sure the children are strictly supervised when making up and using the two-part epoxy adhesive such as Araldite.*

### Previous skills/knowledge needed
The children will need to have worked with modelling media such as Plasticine before and should be familiar with how to shape and texture it. They should have experience of kneading modelling materials.

### Key background information
Formello and Fimo are brightly-coloured modelling media. They can be worked very easily and remain soft until they are baked in a domestic oven. This activity gives children an

**DESIGN AND TECHNOLOGY**

opportunity to work on small intricate items which will help improve their manipulative skills. It also gives them an opportunity to design and make pieces of jewellery for themselves, friends and family. (This activity could be linked with looking at jewellery from other periods of history, and then the children can be asked to make their own products with these characteristics.)

## Vocabulary

Formello, Fimo, Araldite, knead, acetate film.

## Preparation

Ask children to bring in one example of some jewellery which they have at home. They should bring it in a sealed envelope with their name and the type of jewellery clearly marked. Emphasise that it should not be very expensive, and that they should ask permission from their parents if they are borrowing the jewellery. Tell them that it will be required for only one lesson, and that they can take it home the same day. Make some examples of jewellery from the modelling medium of your choice. Have a range of products available – earrings, brooches, necklaces, pendants, bracelets – and include both simple and more complex designs.

## Resources needed

Formello or Fimo, brooch backs, earring clips, Araldite two-part epoxy glue, thin wire, thread, aluminium foil, baking tray, oven, a plastic sheet (not one used for food activities), knife, fork (for texturing), rolling pin, acetate film, coat-hanger wire, stones, beads, pens and paper.

## What to do

As a whole class, take each piece of jewellery from the envelope and discuss it. Record in a table the type of jewellery and its particular features such as what it is made of, what colour it is, whether it is small or chunky. This should give the children an opportunity to start evaluating existing jewellery and give them some ideas for their own products.

Now show the children some of the jewellery that you have made using the modelling material. Tell them that they are going to make a piece of jewellery and they will have to decide who it will be for. (This activity may provide a useful alternative to the ubiquitous Mother's Day card.) Demonstrate to the children the skills and techniques which are required to work with this modelling medium.

The modelling needs to be done on a plastic sheet to prevent sticking. The material needs to be well kneaded before use. Tell them to wash their hands when changing from working with one colour to another. To prevent the medium sticking to a rolling pin, place a piece of clear acetate film over the material and roll on top of it. Show how kneading two or more colours together for a short time gives a marbling effect, and how if you carry on kneading the colours mix together completely.

Shapes can be cut out using a knife. Show how to use a template where they may need to repeat the shape, such as with a pair of earrings. Show children how they can experiment with texture using forks, pastry wheels or by pressing materials like textured fabric or leaves onto the soft material. If you add stones or beads to your jewellery make sure they are made out of materials that will withstand the heat of the oven, and that they are set firmly in a lump of modelling material. You can make shapes, bake them, and then add them to a new uncooked sheet of modelling material, rolling them firmly into place. Beads can be made by making holes in balls of the material with a knitting needle while the material is cold.

The finished product should be put on a sheet of aluminium foil on a baking tray in preparation for baking in an oven at 130°C (275°F) for 15–20 minutes. If you are making beads which you want to be perfect all the way round, thread them onto a piece of coat-hanger wire and shape the wire so that it stands up on the baking sheet while baking. Show children what a product looks like when it comes out of the oven, and how it can be varnished to give a very glossy appearance. Metal earring clips and brooch backs can be stuck on after the products have been baked, using a two-part epoxy glue. This should be done under strict adult supervision.

**DESIGN AND TECHNOLOGY**

Now ask the children to draw out their ideas for jewellery. They should do a large-scale drawing including the use of colour. Ask questions about why they have selected the size, the shape and the colour? Who is it for? They can then make their jewellery. They should be told to produce relatively small pieces. This is not only because the material is quite expensive, but also because the focus in this activity is on more intricate and careful work.

## Suggestion(s) for extension

Children can use wire to create joints to make, for example, 'dangly' earrings.

## Suggestion(s) for support

They can be given some examples of jewellery which you have already made to provide a basis for their design. This allows them to concentrate on the making.

## Assessment opportunities

The quality of the finished product, in terms of its finish and intricacy, will reflect the development of the children's practical skills. The activity also gives an opportunity to compare the children's design ideas with their finished product. Which are the more developed skills – drawing or making?

## Opportunities for IT

The children could use a drawing or art package to create the design for their own jewellery.

## Display ideas

The jewellery should be displayed on the wall together with the children's original design ideas and a description of the person it was made for. You could also include an evaluation from the lucky recipient!

---

# PLASTAZOTE FOR PROTECTION  ◆ FPT

*To develop skills and techniques related to working with Plastazote. To design and make body protection for a chosen leisure activity.*

✝✝ *Working in groups of four.*

🕐 *One two-hour session.*

⚠ *Take care when using a craft knife. Use oven gloves when removing the Plastazote foam from the oven. The foam may get too hot to handle if it is left in the oven for longer than the suggested time.*

## Previous skills/knowledge needed

Children should have cut materials using a craft knife, metal safety rule and cutting mat. They will already have covered methods of joining together textiles, such as laces and buttons.

## Key background information

Plastazote foam consists of a large number of nitrogen bubbles in a large amount of polyethylene (a type of plastic). The bubbles of nitrogen are not connected together so it does not act like a sponge – water cannot get into it. It floats very well (it is used for floats and floating mats in swimming pools), it can be cut easily, and when heated it can be moulded or embossed. This makes it a very versatile material. This activity gives children an opportunity to work with plastics and realise some of their important properties. It also introduces children to the basic techniques required when working with the material in the context of body protection.

## Vocabulary

Plastazote, polyethylene, nitrogen.

## Preparation

Make up a few samples of items using Plastazote foam. They should illustrate how it can be embossed and how it can be welded together by pressure.

## Resources needed

An electric oven, Plastazote foam, craft knives, paper drill, hole punch, hot melt glue gun, clear non-solvent based adhesive, cutting mat, laces, Velcro, zips, buttons, a copy of photocopiable sheet 138 for each child.

## What to do

Ask the children to discuss the following in groups:

▲ What injuries can occur when playing sports?

▲ Are some sports more dangerous than others?

▲ What injuries have children in the group had when playing in the playground?

▲ Which part of the body gets injured most frequently?

▲ Which part of the body needs to be protected the most?

Discuss the groups' findings as a whole class. The head will probably come out as the part of the body that is most in need of protection. Point out head-wear already being worn by sports people (in motor racing, rock climbing, bicycle riding, cricket). Go on to discuss other injuries which are commonplace. Grazed knees and elbows are likely to be high on the list.

Give each person in the class a piece of Plastazote and ask them to look at it carefully and then describe some feature about it (for example: it is light, colourful, flexible). Then demonstrate some of its other properties. Cut it using a craft knife, metal safety rule and cutting board. Show the children how it can be heated in an electric oven and how it becomes soft making it mouldable into different shapes. (Electric oven at 150°C for about ten seconds per millimetre thickness of foam.) Give them a copy of photocopiable sheet 138 which illustrates some techniques for working with the material. Explain that as it cools it stays in the new shape but can be returned to its original flat shape by placing it in the oven for a minute or so. Show them how it can be embossed by pressing a shape into the heated material, and how two pieces can be welded together if they are pushed firmly together when they are hot.

Explain that this material is suitable to provide body protection for sport. Ask each group to identify a particular sport or leisure interest and to decide on a part of the body which this material could be used to protect. Remind the children of ways of joining together parts of clothes, for example, using a lace, Velcro, buttons or a zip. Encourage them to experiment with the material and paper patterns, and then to select ways of fixing the protection to the body.

At the end of the activity, each group wears the body protection, acting out the sport for which it was devised. The rest of the class can then ask questions about the product. Once all the groups have demonstrated their body protection, each child can be asked to write down a positive and a negative feature of each product. This gives an opportunity for evaluating new products in a relatively supportive way.

### Suggestion(s) for extension
Develop the product further by, perhaps, embossing the 'company' (or school) logo onto the device, or working on the overall 'look' of the product as well as its functionality.

### Suggestions for support
Some samples of possible elbow and knee protectors could be available for children to look at.

### Assessment opportunities
The ability to evaluate can be assessed when the children identify positive and negative features of each other's products. Opportunities also exist to see if children have understood the need for comfort, practicality and movability.

### Display ideas
Place on a table the finished body protector. Place pictures of people doing the sport where the injury occurs, together with the children's evaluations on the wall behind the table.

### Reference to photocopiable sheet
Sheet 138 shows the techniques which need to be used when working with Plastazote. This sheet should form a useful reference when children use Plastazote in any activity.

## HAND-MADE POTTERY ◆ FPT

*To develop skills and techniques related to working with clay.*

†† *Working individually.*

🕒 *Two one-hour sessions.*

⚠ *Make sure that hands are washed after working with clay and that the approriate protective clothing is worn.*

### Previous skills/knowledge needed
Children may well have done work with clay before in either art or design and technology. The activity assumes little previous knowledge, but it could be used to revise the techniques and to make children aware that clay is a material they should consider when designing and making.

### Key background information
This activity aims to introduce children to a few simple techniques needed when working with clay.

DESIGN AND TECHNOLOGY

## Vocabulary

Coiling, slabbing, fired, slip, pinching.

## Preparation

Clay should be broken up into relatively small pieces. The tables should be covered with plastic sheeting with a hardboard placed on top.

## Resources needed

Clay, plastic sheeting, hardboard, container with slip and a brush, wooden clay tools, glaze, kiln.

## What to do

Tell the group that they are going to make some pots out of clay in order to practise four important techniques – kneading, pinching, coiling and slabbing. Demonstrate the techniques to the children.

▲ *Kneading.* Press the heels of your hands onto the clay, pushing away from your body. Then pull the clay up towards your body and repeat the pressing movement. This should be continued for a minute or so (see Figure 6.1). Emphasise the importance of this technique for making the clay pliable and for pushing all the air out of it. If air remains, the pot can explode when it is fired.

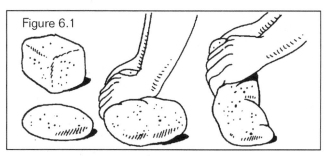

Figure 6.1

▲ *Pinching.* Start by putting your thumb into the centre of a small ball of clay and making an indentation. Then pinch the clay between your finger and thumb and slowly turn the clay with the other hand (see Figure 6.2). Gradually a hemispherical pot can be made.

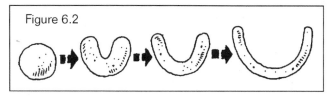

Figure 6.2

▲ *Coiling.* Roll out the clay and cut out a circular shape for the base of the pot. Put some grooves into the base around the edge and brush a mixture of water with a little clay in it (called 'slip') over them. Roll out some more clay to form a long sausage shape. Using this make a coil around the base, covering each layer of coil with slip and pressing down firmly so that each one is stuck firmly to the next. Gradually build the pot up, then smooth out the coils by using your hands and a wooden clay tool. You can make different shapes by changing the positions of the coils (see Figure 6.3).

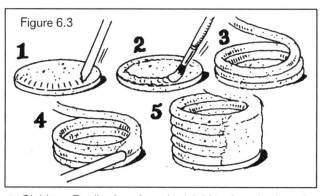

Figure 6.3

▲ *Slabbing.* Finally show how the 'slabbing' method can be used to make a straight-sided pot. Roll out the clay using a rolling pin. Cut it up into five suitable pieces (one base and four walls). Brush slip around the edges of the base. Roll a thin sausage of clay and press it down between the base and one of the walls, using your hands and a wooden clay tool. Repeat with the remaining sides (see Figure 6.4).

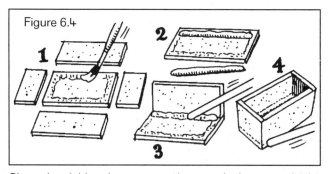

Figure 6.4

Show the children how to use glaze, and what a pot looks like after it is fired. The children should now practise these techniques and make three small containers. They should experiment with decorating using clay tools and glaze and finally, their work should be fired in a kiln.

**DESIGN AND TECHNOLOGY**

## Suggestion(s) for extension

Children should be encouraged to research into the designs of pottery from a particular period of history, or from another country or civilisation which they might be covering in geography, history or religious education. The pots that they subsequently make should have characteristics based on their research.

## Suggestion(s) for support

Children who are having difficulty should concentrate on the slab method of construction, with the pieces having been marked out and cut by the teacher. When they have gained confidence they should go on to the pinching method.

## Assessment opportunities

At a basic level, you will be able to assess the level of skill the children have in working with clay, and identify strengths and weaknesses. Those who engage in the extension activity can be assessed on their ability to evaluate other people's work and to use it to assist them in their own designs.

## Opportunities for IT

The children could use a CD-ROM to research information about pots from different periods of history or other cultures. Different groups of children could use a word processor to write a sequence of instructions for display in the classroom about, for example, kneading clay or making a pinch pot.

A different approach would be to use a multi-media authoring package to create an electronic presentation about using clay. This could link together textual and pictorial information about making pots. Pictures of children making the pots could be included either taken with a digital camera, or scanned from photographs taken in the class. It is also possible to include short video sequences in some software. The children can make a short recorded commentary using a microphone attached to the computer.

## Display ideas

Three areas of the classroom should be set up with the pots made by the three different methods grouped together. The tables should be labelled 'Pinching', 'Coiling' and 'Slabbing' and children should add to the tables word-processed cards saying what they found easy and what they found hard about making the pots.

## DOUGH PLAQUES     FPT

***To develop skills and techniques related to working with salt dough.***

†† *Working individually.*

🕐 *Two one-hour sessions.*

⚠ *As you are working with food materials it is appropriate to use equipment designated only for food use in this activity (that is, the table covering, children's aprons, rolling pin, knife, fork, mixing bowls, pastry brushes). Ensure that Plasticine, varnish and paint are not available to the children when this equipment is being used. Oven gloves must be used for putting in and taking out the models.*

## Previous skills/knowledge needed

Children will need to be familiar with working with a modelling medium such as Plasticine.

## Key background information

The South American Indians were apparently the first people to use bread dough to create ornaments. They lived in Ecuador, and as they had little access to clay, they made use of bread dough instead. During the Second World War women made bread-dough jewellery, but it often turned mouldy! This activity introduces children to working in this medium by producing products which are often found at craft fairs.

## Vocabulary

Dough, knead, plaque.

### Working with bread dough

this animal shape is made of pieces of dough stuck together

a sharp instrument can be used to make marks in the dough

twist of dough to form handle

large plaited loaf

simple roll — ball of dough with cross cut in top

twist of dough to form base

use a fork to texture the basket

put dough through a mincer or garlic press to give this hair effect

**DESIGN AND TECHNOLOGY**

# Mouldable materials

## Preparation

*The recipe for salt dough is:* three cups of plain flour, one cup of salt, one cup of water and a teaspoon of cooking oil. The ingredients should be mixed to form a dough. It should then be kneaded for a couple of minutes. Leave it for half an hour before it is used. The salt dough can be stored for up to a day in a sealed plastic bag. It is probably better to make it in bulk, rather than letting children make it on an individual basis – at least to start with. You should prepare some samples of salt dough products.

## Resources needed

Plasticine, covering for table, salt dough (salt, plain flour, cooking oil and water) made up in plastic bags for each child, an oven, aluminium foil, baking tray, knife, fork, pastry brush, dish of water, container for flour, rolling pins, polyurethane high gloss varnish, brush, a copy of photocopiable sheet 139 for children who need support.

## What to do

Introduce the activity by showing the children some of the products that can be made from salt dough. Ask if any of the class have been to craft fairs and seen similar products. Tell the group that they are going to put on a craft fair for parents one afternoon and that they need to make lots of salt dough plaques to sell. They need to think of a theme for their plaque – will it contain someone's name, or will it illustrate a hobby?

Demonstrate the basic techniques. The models should be made on a sheet of aluminium foil. This can easily be transferred to the baking sheet and then the oven. Use a little flour to prevent the dough from sticking to the foil. Take small pieces of dough out of the plastic bag as required. Re-knead each piece of dough as it is used. Use a rolling pin to flatten the dough if necessary. Use a pastry brush and water to stick the different pieces of dough together. When the model is finished it needs to be baked in an oven at 150°C (300°F) for about an hour. This, however, is merely a guide. It must be brown but not burned, and it must be totally dry or it will not keep. Show the children that models can be painted using ordinary water paint and then varnished.

Now ask the children to design and practise making and texturing the product using Plasticine as a modelling medium, working on their own design. When you are happy that they have a reasonable prototype, they can put away the Plasticine, cover the desk with a waterproof covering, get a plastic bag of dough, container of water and pastry brush, a container of flour, a knife, a fork, a piece of aluminium foil, and start making their plaque.

## Suggestion(s) for extension

Using the same techniques, children can design and make other products using salt dough. There are many books available with sources of ideas for salt-dough models.

## Suggestion(s) for support

Children could be given a copy of photocopiable sheet 139 to give them some more ideas. More detailed one-to-one demonstrations of the techniques could be given to some children, which they could be encouraged to copy carefully. It might be that this is a small group activity which takes place at the same time as other non-practical tasks within the classroom.

## Assessment opportunities

The quality of the finished products can be assessed, giving a measure of the skills and techniques which the children have developed during the activity.

## Opportunities for IT

The children could use a word processor or desktop publishing package to make price labels or advertising information for the craft fair sale stall.

## Display ideas

The presentation of the products in the classroom in preparation for the craft fair sale will form the basis of the display. Small neat price labels and advertising material can be added to the stall.

## Reference to photoocpiable sheet

Sheet 139 shows some of the techniques which can be used when working with salt dough, and is to be used as support material only.

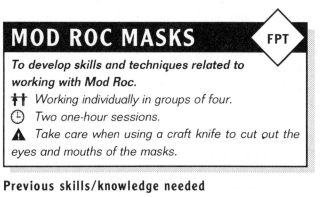

# MOD ROC MASKS    FPT

*To develop skills and techniques related to working with Mod Roc.*

†† *Working individually in groups of four.*

🕐 *Two one-hour sessions.*

⚠ *Take care when using a craft knife to cut out the eyes and mouths of the masks.*

## Previous skills/knowledge needed

Children should know how to use a craft knife, and will have done previous modelling with papier mâché (for example, the activity on page 48).

## Key background information

Mod Roc is plaster impregnated into pieces of bandage. It enables plaster to be used creating less mess than would be the case using traditional plaster of Paris. The children are to make masks for an end-of-term party. Leave the design of the masks open to the children's own individual interests.

## Vocabulary

Mod Roc, plaster of Paris.

**DESIGN AND TECHNOLOGY**

## Preparation

You will need examples or pictures of masks from different times and cultures. Collect different materials for the children to build up their moulds with, for example: cardboard, Plasticine, pieces of plastic.

## Resources needed

A copy of photocopiable sheet 140 per child, pencils and paper, Mod Roc, scissors, craft knife, container of tepid water, glasspaper, paint, paintbrushes, varnish, hardboard, range of materials for mould, basic plastic mask, Vaseline, chicken wire, newspaper, aprons.

## What to do

Ask the children if they have ever heard of masked balls. These were like fancy dress parties, but only the faces of the guests were (dressed up) covered, so that people did not know who they were dancing with until midnight, when everyone removed her or his mask. If appropriate, say that you have arranged for them to have an end-of-term party, where everyone will be wearing masks.

Show the children a few masks to give them some ideas. In groups of four get them to brainstorm some ideas as to what the masks could represent. Emphasise that they are not just to cover the face, but they should actually look like somebody or something, perhaps a pirate, a policeman or some kind of animal... the list should be endless. Discuss the ideas as a class, and then let each child decide on what her or his mask will be. Initial sketches should be looked at by you before the children start making their masks. Go through the procedure, which is outlined on photocopiable sheet 140, and then give each child a copy. Remind them that all the masks need to be complete finished by the day of the party!

## Suggestion(s) for extension

Children could be asked to make some other product which would fit in with the theme of their mask.

## Suggestion(s) for support

A few suggestions could be given, perhaps with some drawings or photographs of possible ideas. More detailed demonstrations could be given to small groups.

## Assessment opportunities

The quality of the finished product gives an indication of the level of skill which children have when working with this material. This activity also gives an opportunity to assess how creative the children's ideas were and how effective they were at putting them into practice.

## Opportunities for IT

Children could use a CD-ROM encyclopaedia to research ideas for different forms of masks.

## Display ideas

The party itself will be an opportunity to display the masks, and perhaps they could put on a mask fashion display for a school assembly. It could be turned into a competition, where children in the school write down what they think the different masks are supposed to represent. The results could be displayed pictorially using graphing software and then placed on a wall display alongside the masks – a useful form of external evaluation.

## Reference to photocopiable sheet

Sheet 140 shows how to use Mod Roc to produce a mask.

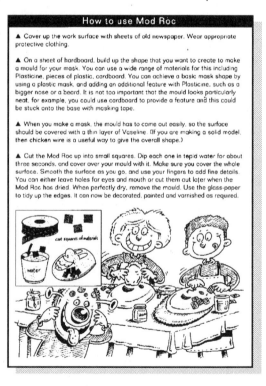

# Food

This section includes an activity on food hygiene and safety, an investigation into the labelling of food and some techniques for evaluating the popularity of particular food products.

Many of the activities focus upon how the food materials can be combined and mixed together and the ways in which the working characteristics of materials can be used to greatest effect.

The food stuffs that are used can easily be altered to give children different experiences. For example, instead of evaluating soups you could substitute yoghurts, or instead of developing bread roll recipes, a similar activity could be done in the context of biscuits.

Many of the activities focus upon how the food materials can be combined and mixed together. Depending on the characteristics of the materials, children will find out appropriate methods of cutting, stirring, mixing and shaping. They will also learn about testing food products and making decisions about the types of taste and texture which they prefer.

## FOOD HYGIENE   ◇ IDEA

*To make children aware of the importance of food hygiene and safety.*

†† *Whole class and then individuals.*

🕐 *Two one-hour sessions.*

### Previous skills/knowledge needed
This activity builds upon and extends the work the children will have done on food safety and hygiene at Key Stage 1.

### Key background information
Too often, learning about food safety and hygiene can be very boring, so this activity attempts to make it amusing and memorable for the children.

### Vocabulary
Anti-bacterial, bacteria.

### Preparation
Use photocopiable sheet 141 as the basis for a differentiated worksheet. First photocopy the sheet as it is. Then, using correcting fluid, remove the key words and replace them with a dash. You now have two sheets, one complete and one with key words missing. It is clearly possible to differentiate still further by removing a greater range of words. (Ensure that the sheet used for the main activity is clearly more difficult than the one used for the support activity.) You also need to prepare some very dirty cloths, aprons, towels, utensils and bowls. Enlist the help of one or two children in the class, in particular, one who has long hair. A 'joke shop' finger would be useful.

### Resources needed
A selection of clean equipment that is used for working with food, differently coloured Plasticine, plastic table cloths, flesh- and blue-coloured Elastoplast, handkerchief, anti-bacterial cleaner, the 'special' dirty equipment, a copy of photocopiable sheet 141 per child.

### What to do
The aim of this session is to give the class an amusing demonstration of what *not* to do in terms of food hygiene and safety, and to highlight the reasons for the rules that they must abide by. With the help of your two assistants, prepare a fruit salad. Do not use real food as this would inevitably have to be wasted – fruit made from Plasticine would be appropriate. Your two assistants should have dirty hands, dirty aprons, hair hanging in the food, and be coughing and sneezing all over it. They should wash their hands and then wipe them on a dirty towel. They should (pretend to) cut their finger, put on a skin-coloured bandage, and lose it in the fruit bowl, to be found as you try the fruit salad.

At the end of the role-play, the class should be asked what was wrong and how things should be changed. As the class mention each problem and solution, it should be put right. For example: when they say that aprons should be clean, your assistants change their aprons; when they are told they should not cough or sneeze over food, they get out a big handkerchief and use it; and when they cut themselves they put on a big blue dressing so that it can be seen clearly in food if it drops off. By the end of the class discussion your two assistants should appear perfectly prepared for working safely and hygienically with food.

Now give each child a copy of photocopiable sheet 141. Ask them to fill in the missing words on their sheet to consolidate what they learned in the session.

### Suggestion(s) for extension
The children can be given a more difficult differentiated sheet which contains only a few words and add their own food safety and hygiene notes to the page. They could add illustrations to their notes and also illustrate the notes on the original photocopiable sheet.

### Suggestion(s) for support
Less able children could be given another differentiated sheet which has only a few key words missing, which the children have to add.

### Assessment opportunities
The correctly completed sheet will identify that children are aware of the safety and hygiene rules which are so important when working with food.

### Opportunities for IT
The children could use a word processor or desktop publishing package to produce a set of food hygiene instructions for display in the classroom. These could also include pictures, drawn using an art package, taken from clip art collections or scanned from the children's own line drawings.

**DESIGN AND TECHNOLOGY**

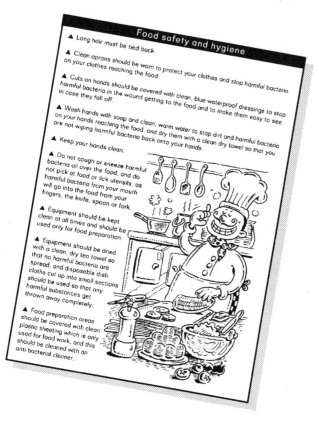

## Display ideas

Produce a large version of the photocopiable sheet 141 which they filled in for wall mounting. They could use the illustrations done for extension and use a DTP program for the text.

## Reference to photocopiable sheet

Sheet 141 illustrates the important aspects of food safety and hygiene which it is vital that the children are familiar with when working with food. It is to be used as the basis of a series of differentiated sheets.

## EVALUATING READY-MADE SOUP  ◆ IDEA

*To teach children methods of evaluating the preferences of people for different products.*

✝✝ *Working in groups of four.*

🕐 *Two one-hour sessions.*

⚠ *Make sure children are aware of the importance of food hygiene when they are working on this activity.*

## Previous skills/knowledge needed

Children should have undertaken an activity which emphasises aspects of food hygiene and safety which they need to consider during this session. They should be familiar with the idea of evaluation, although not necessarily within the context of food.

## Key background information

This activity introduces the children to two methods of analysing how much a product is liked. These techniques can be used either to evaluate existing products (for example, which is the most popular soup, so that it could be put on the school dinner menu), or to evaluate new products which the children have designed to see which ones are worth developing further.

## Vocabulary

Analysis, questionnaire, texture, consistency, evaluation.

## Preparation

You need to select a wide range of soups from different manufacturers and of different types (packet, tinned and carton), for the children to evaluate. You can choose to evaluate different makes of the same flavour of soup like a *Which?* consumer survey. However, as an introduction to the techniques it might be more interesting for the children to taste lots of flavours and makes of soup rather than being restricted to one. Photocopiable sheet 142 needs to be cut in half, separating the two forms. A copy of each form will be needed for each of the four food tests completed, so each child will need eight forms altogether.

## Resources needed

A selection of packet, tinned and carton soups, small plastic drinks containers, microwave, hot plate, computer, printer, copies of the forms on photocopiable sheet 142.

## What to do

Ask one child to taste some soup blindfolded. Ask her what she thinks of it. Discuss with the rest of the class her use of language. Did she say 'nice' or 'disgusting'? Could the taste have been described in other ways that might tell people a little bit more about the soup (for example: thick, tastes like tomatoes, creamy).

When food manufacturers are testing new flavours they have to ask people what they think about the new products. Tell the children that they are going to try two methods of evaluating different kinds of soup. The first method *describes* how much you prefer one product to another. The second method *attempts to measure* how much you like a particular product. Explain to the children that the information is usually obtained by doing food tests and using a questionnaire. Discuss the information that might be required. As a class, brainstorm ideas such as what it looks like, what it smells like, what it tastes like. By questioning you should encourage children to think about colour, appearance, smell, taste, texture, creaminess and consistency. They should also consider a wide range of words to describe the taste, flavour, smell, appearance and texture of soups. Get them to brainstorm words such as dry, salty, sickly, sour, spicy, sweet, tasteless, greasy, lumpy, powdery, thick, thin and watery. Also discuss the possible responses such as 'liked it a lot' or 'disgusting'.

**Product evaluation questionnaire**

Date _____

Name _____

Tester Male/Female     Age _____

Type of product _____

Please look at the product.

I like it very much     I quite like it     It is OK     I dislike it quite a lot     I dislike it a lot

Now smell the product. What did you think?

I like it very much     I quite like it     It is OK     I dislike it quite a lot     I dislike it a lot

What do you think about the flavour of the product?

I like it very much     I quite like it     It is OK     I dislike it quite a lot     I dislike it a lot

What do you think about the texture of the product?

I like it very much     I quite like it     It is OK     I dislike it quite a lot     I dislike it a lot

What do you think of the product overall?

I like it very much     I quite like it     It is OK     I dislike it quite a lot     I dislike it a lot

**Product analysis sheet**

Date _____

Name _____

▲ Look at each food sample. Consider each of the following features of the food. Give a score between 1 and 9 in each section of the table. (1 represents VERY BAD and 9 represents VERY GOOD) Then add up the totals in each column to give a comparison.

| | Product W | Product N | Product R |
|---|---|---|---|
| Colour | | | |
| Smell | | | |
| Taste | | | |
| Thickness | | | |
| Texture | | | |
| Creaminess | | | |
| Overall appearance | | | |
| TOTALS | | | |

Give them a copy of the 'Product evaluation questionnaire' from photocopiable sheet 142 and put them in groups of four. Explain how each group will run its tasting panel. The samples of soup should be in small plastic containers which are the same size and shape. They should all be served at the same temperature. The samples can be labelled using numbers, letters or shapes but they should not be labelled simply 'A, B, C, D' or '1, 2, 3, 4' as this suggests a preferred order. It is important to emphasise that you are expecting the children to say which sample they like. There is no right or wrong answer, but you are trying to find out which sample is the most popular. Explain that when a company is spending a lot of money on a new product they want to make sure that enough people will buy it. They have to ask a large sample group to ensure they get a true pictures of how many people like the product.

The groups can now undertake the food test using four different soups. Each child tests each soup, so each group will have a total of sixteen questionnaires to complete. When they have finished testing, each group should look at the questionnaires and analyse them.

They then bring their findings back to the whole class. A large range of questions can be asked. Was there a most popular soup? Did girls like some soups more than boys? Was one soup disliked by everyone? The discussion should lead to the idea that it is quite difficult to answer some of these questions because of the way in which the questionnaire asked very general questions. For example, one taster may have disliked the smell, liked the texture and said it was OK overall. A second person may again have thought it was OK overall, disliked the texture, but thought

the flavour was excellent. The general comment about the product overall is too subjective and does not really help in deciding on the most popular characteristics. Suggest that it might be better to use an approach which attempts to measure, using numbers, how popular a particular product is if you want more detailed information.

Show the children the 'Product analysis sheet'. This requires the testers to give a score from 1 to 9 for each property and allows for comparison. Ask the children to repeat the food test using the same samples, but now recording the information on this sheet. Ask the groups to look at their findings and again report back to the whole class. The second technique should make it much easier to find the most and the least popular soups.

The children can now do one final test using different soup samples and using the method of their choice. They should be encouraged to improve the recording sheet that they decide to use.

### Suggestion(s) for extension
Children could design their own recording sheets from the start rather than using the ones from sheet 142.

### Suggestion(s) for support
By carefully selecting the groups of four so that they contain a mixture of abilities, the more able children will be able to support the weaker ones in the analysis.

### Assessment opportunities
This activity gives an opportunity to identify the ability of children to analyse data which has been collected from the food tests. If children are able to improve upon the tables when they redesign them or design their own, it is clear they have a good understanding of what information they need to collect.

SOUPER CHEF.

## Opportunities for IT

The children could use a computer database to record and analyse their findings in the initial tasting test. The database could be set up with the following fieldnames:

| | |
|---|---|
| Soup | tomato |
| Taster | Joanne |
| Gender | female |
| Taste | good |
| Consistency | watery |
| Look | ·lumpy |
| Overall | average |

It is important to make sure that there is some consistency in the vocabulary used to describe the soups. A good way to do this is for the class to draw up, from the list of brainstormed descriptive words, those which they are going to use. Some databases allow children to use tokenised fields where only agreed responses can be selected.

Once the database has been completed the children can use it to look at questions such as:

Which were the most preferred soups?

Did girls have different tastes from boys?

The results can also be displayed pictorially using the graphical facilities of the database. It would be easy to record the whole class's data on a single spreadsheet and use a formula to record the averages or the range of scores for each soup.

## Display ideas

Produce large posters incorporating the record sheets, the groups' analysis of their database and the packaging (label or packet) from the selected soups.

## Reference to photocopiable sheet

Sheet 142 provides two sample record sheets to assist with food testing. The headings have been kept general so that the same sheets could be used as a basis for testing many different samples of food.

## FOOD LABELLING
### IDEA

*To understand what a food label tells us.*

†† *Working in pairs*

🕐 *Two one-hour sessions.*

## Previous skills/knowledge needed

It would be helpful if children have already looked at the different kinds of food in their science work and are aware of the terms carbohydrate, protein and fat.

## Key background information

The labels on food products are often confusing, but they are able to give a great deal of information. This activity gives children an opportunity to find out what some of it means.

## Vocabulary

Protein, carbohydrate, fat, additive.

## Preparation

Children should be asked a fortnight prior to this lesson to bring in the labels from a wide range of food products. Have a few products available, in case some children forget. Select one or two of your own to use in the introductory session. Boxes of breakfast cereal tend to have a great deal of information included on them.

## Resources needed

A wide selection of food packaging brought in by the children, plain paper, adhesive, writing materials.

## What to do

Introduce the idea of obtaining information from packaging. Read out some of the information on the packaging of your choice to see the sort of information that is available. Ask the children to give examples of the following from their own packaging as you go through this class discussion.

▲ *Name of the food:* This might be a general term like lasagne or green beans, or a specific trade mark like Coco Pops or Clover.

▲ *Ingredients:* This is what is actually in the food product. It does not say how much of each substance there is, but they have to be written in order, with the substance of which there is most at the beginning of the list. Notice that water is often listed. On many containers the ingredients are in very small writing. Why? Does the information help you when you decide to buy a particular product?

▲ *Shelf-life:* This means how long it can be kept. 'Use by _____' will be found on goods which will only last a short time, such as fresh milk, meat or chilled meals. 'Best before _____' will be found on food products that will last much longer – a chocolate cake in a box or a piece of cheese

DESIGN AND TECHNOLOGY

sealed in plastic are examples of these. 'Best before end _____' will be found on products that will last a very long time, such as cereals contained in airtight waxed paper bags (inside cardboard boxes) or tomato sauce in a bottle.

▲ *Storage instructions:* This is where special storage instructions are given, such as 'keep in the fridge' or 'cannot be frozen' – this might be because it contains substances that separate once they are frozen.

▲ *The name and address of the manufacturer/packer/seller:* This is important so that you know who to write to if there is something wrong with the product, or if you think it is delicious and want to congratulate the manufacturer!

▲ *Weight or volume of food:* This is so you know how much there should be in the packet without opening it. It also lets you compare prices more easily if you know that two packages contain the same quantity.

▲ *Cooking/preparation instructions:* This is so you know what to do with the product in case you have not bought it before.

▲ *Bar code:* This is so the price of the product can be checked by the computer at the check-out. It saves people labelling each product with a price, and it is much easier to change the price quickly. It also helps with stock control.

▲ *Nutritional information:* This tells you how much carbohydrate, protein, fat and vitamins there are in the product. Explain that a balanced diet contains some of each kind of food, and that it is important not to eat just one type all the time. Breakfast cereals, in particular, are often advertised as providing a good proportion of all types of food.

By looking carefully at a label such as that found on breakfast cereals, you can see how much protein, carbohydrate, fat, fibre, sodium, vitamins and energy you are getting from a bowl of milk and cereal.

| Typical values | Per 100g of cereal | Serving of 30g with 125ml of *semi-skimmed* milk |
|---|---|---|
| Energy | 1565 kJ | 713kJ |
|  | 369 kcal | 169 kcal |
| Protein | 7.9g | 6.5g |
| Carbohydrate | 75.9g | 28.7g |
| of which sugars | 22.4g | 12.7g |
| Fat | 3.8g | 3.1g |
| of which saturates | 1.5g | 1.8g |
| Fibre | 6.2g | 1.8g |
| Sodium | 0.8g | 0.3g |

| Vitamins | Per 100g of cereal | | Serving of 30g with 125ml of *skimmed* milk | |
|---|---|---|---|---|
|  |  | %RDA |  | %RDA |
| Vitamin C | 51.0mg | 85 | 16.4mg | 25 |
| Thiamin (B1) | 1.2mg | 85 | 0.4mg | 25 |
| Riboflavin (B2) | 1.4mg | 85 | 0.6mg | 35 |
| Niacin | 15.3 mg | 85 | 4.7mg | 25 |
| Vitamin B6 | 1.7mg | 85 | 0.5mg | 25 |
| Folacin | 170.0µg | 85 | 51.0µg | 25 |
| Vitamin B12 | 0.85µg | 85 | 0.6µg | 60 |
| Pantothenic acid | 5.1mg | 85 | 1.9mg | 30 |

Recommended daily allowance (RDA) according to the EC Nutrition Labelling Directive 90/496/EEC.

Point out that the data shows that most of the cereal is carbohydrate. It also shows that one portion gives us one-quarter of our daily requirements of most of the vitamins. The above shows the detail that you may find on some typical cereal packaging. Having discussed the importance of each part of the labelling, the children should stick the information from their product into the centre of a piece of paper and then explain the purpose of each element for their particular example.

### Suggestion(s) for extension

Children can design their own labels for a product of their choice. They need to select carefully the information they wish to include and consider how to make the label appealing to encourage people to buy it. They also need to consider issues such as font size – should the product name be larger than the text on nutritional information. A DTP package could be used by some children for this activity.

### Suggestion(s) for support

The children could concentrate less on the nutritional information and more on the other aspects of the labelling which is generally much easier to analyse.

### Assessment opportunities

The children's written work will identify whether or not they understand the information found on food packaging, and what it is there for.

### Opportunities for IT

The children could use a drawing or desktop publishing package to display information about their particular food graphically. If the latter is used, the children can create a frame for each part of the label and move the frames around the page to position them to the label. They will need to know how to create, re-size and position frames, write and format text within the frame and add a border. Some DTP packages enable children to draw linking lines to the central title. The results might look something like this:

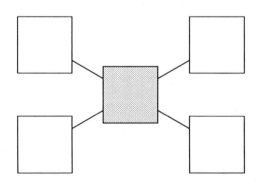

Similar results can be obtained using a drawing package where the children can use the text facility to add labels, add a frame to the text and then draw lines to link it to the central label.

An alternative approach would be to create an electronic presentation of the information using a multi-media authoring package. The teacher could set up the structure in advance with a title page that consisted of a list of the different foods. Each child or pair could design two or three linked pages about their food. The information could contain text, numerical data, pictures scanned from the children's own drawings, or drawn using an art package. It might even be possible to link together certain ingredients from each package so that children could click on 'fibre' and be shown the fibre content of each food, for example. Some packages, like GENESIS, have a database facility to make this easier. Undertake this type of work when there is extra support available in the classroom.

### Display ideas
The children's work can be wall mounted with examples of the packaging displayed below on a table.

## MAKING BUTTER  ◆ FPT

*To make children aware of a method of changing the texture and taste of a food product.*

**♦♦** *Whole class working in pairs.*

**◷** *1 hour.*

**⚠** *All the equipment used in this activity should be used only for working with food. Desks should be covered with plastic-coated fabric and cleaned with anti-bacterial spray before the work starts. Children should be reminded of all the food hygiene and safety rules. They should wash their hands and wear protective clothing.*

### Previous skills/knowledge needed
Children should have undertaken activities which focus upon hygiene and food safety.

### Key background information
Butter is made from cream by a process called churning. This means that the cream is shaken until it splits into a liquid called buttermilk and a solid called butter. This activity gives the children an opportunity to see how one particular technique can be used to transform one food product into another. It also provides a context to a possible design and make activity where children are required to mechanise the butter-making process.

### Vocabulary
Buttermilk, churning.

### Preparation
The cream and the screw-top jars should be cooled in a refrigerator for at least an hour prior to the lesson. This will ensure that you make as much butter as possible from a small quantity of cream.

### Resources needed
Each pair requires 150ml of fresh double cream, salt, a screw-top jar, knife, fork, wooden board, wooden spoon, aluminium foil, two slices of bread, packaging from other spreads, one copy of photocopiable sheet 143 per child, access to some weighing scales.

### What to do
Talk about butter and other spreads such as margarine, low fat and so on. What are they made from? (This element of the activity can be extended by looking at the details on the packages.) Emphasise the importance of a good standard of food hygiene and then demonstrate to the children how to make butter.

Pour 150ml cream into the cooled screw-top jar. Screw the lid on. Shake the jar until the butter separates from the buttermilk. This should take about five to ten minutes. Unscrew the jar, and carefully pour off the buttermilk. Add a tablespoonful of cold water to the butter in the jar, then mix with a fork and pour off the extra liquid. Take the butter out of the jar and put it on a wooden board. Add a pinch of salt and then pat it into a block shape using wooden spoons or spatulas. Wrap the block of butter in foil and place it in a refrigerator until it is cool.

Give each pair a copy of photocopiable page 143 which illustrates the butter-making process. Ask them to make their own portion of butter. Let them butter a slice of bread with their own butter so they can eat it at lunch-time or playtime.

**DESIGN AND TECHNOLOGY**

## Suggestion(s) for extension

The children could design packaging for their small portion of butter of the type seen in cafés and restaurants.

## Suggestion(s) for support

Children may require help to measure the double cream accurately, but are likely to cope effectively with the rest of the activity.

Making butter from cream

① Measure 150 ml of cream on the scales.

② Pour cream into cooled jar.

③ Screw the lid on tightly. Shake the jar until the cream begins to separate.

④ Unscrew the lid and pour off the liquid – this is called buttermilk.

⑤ Add a tablespoon of cold water to the jar.

⑥ Mix the butter and water together using a fork.

⑦ Take the butter out of the jar and make it into a neat shape. Add a little salt if you want to.

⑧ Wrap the butter in some aluminium foil and put it into a refrigerator.

⑨ Now try your home-made butter on some toast!

## Assessment opportunities

This activity identifies the ability of children to follow diagrammatic instructions.

## Opportunities for IT

The children could use an art or drawing package to design their own butter label. They could also use a word processor to write instructions on how to make butter. They can use the 'cut and paste' or 'drag and drop' commands to move instructions around to get them into the correct sequence. The final set of instructions can be formatted, printed and used for a classroom display.

## Display ideas

Put on the wall as many different labels and packages of butter, margarine and other spreads as the children can bring in. Produce large labels with the names of the ingredients of the various products and add them to the display.

## Reference to photocopiable sheet

Sheet 143 shows in diagrammatic form how to produce butter from cream.

---

## BREAD ROLLS    FPT

*To follow instructions and measure accurately.*
*To adapt recipes to appeal to particular people.*
†† *Working in pairs.*
🕓 *One two-hour session.*
⚠ *All the equipment used in this activity should only be used for working with food. Desks should be covered with plastic-coated fabric and cleaned with anti-bacterial spray before the work starts. Children should be reminded of food hygiene and safety rules.*

### Previous skills/knowledge needed

Children should have covered work on hygiene and safety before starting this activity. They should also have looked at methods of evaluating food products.

### Key background information

This activity gives children an opportunity to explore the changes that take place when yeast is added to flour and water. The production of carbon dioxide gas when the yeast reacts, makes the dough rise. This produces the particular light texture we associate with bread. By adding a limited number of additional ingredients and by looking at the way in which the dough can be worked into different shapes, children can be taught that a basic recipe can easily be transformed into more unusual products.

### Vocabulary

Knead, texture, carbon dioxide, dough, yeast.

### Preparation

You will need to collect samples of different bread products from a wide range of different cultures, for example: naan, pitta, ciabatta, baguette, tin loaf.

### Resources needed

Variety of breads, flour (white, granary, wholemeal), yeast, sugar, variety of spices and herbs, onion, garlic, cheese, mixed fruit, nuts and seeds, mixing bowls, spoons, measuring jugs, weighing scales, graters, small knives, chopping boards, baking trays, plastic table covers, plastic aprons, access to cooker.

### What to do

Start the lesson by showing the children the wide selection of bread products which you have collected. Focus upon the shape, the smell and the texture rather than tasting them at this stage. What is it that makes it a bread? Discuss the fact that yeast is not required for all bread (pitta bread). Basically, it is a flour dough that makes it bread.

Tell the children that each pair is going to make four bread rolls. Each roll should be a different shape, and have slightly different features. Talk to the children about the basic ingredients for their bread rolls.

DESIGN AND TECHNOLOGY

A typical recipe would be:
500g flour
250ml warm water
1 level teaspoon salt
2 tablespoons sunflower oil
1 packet of yeast

Write the recipe on the board (see above). Demonstrate how to mix the ingredients together in a large mixing bowl, and how to knead the dough. Leave it to rise for approximately 20 minutes – longer if possible, place it on a baking sheet and then put it in the oven at 225°C (450°F) for 15–20 minutes.

Now show them the range of 'extra' ingredients that you have available. To avoid having the children just 'throw in' any ingredient, get them to discuss in their pairs what each of the rolls will look like and who it will particularly appeal to. Ask them to write down and draw their ideas which you can comment on before they make and bake their bread rolls. When the rolls are cooked the pairs can taste them. (They must be careful not to burn their tongues.) Ask them to write down what they think of their rolls.

## Suggestion(s) for extension

A food evaluation test could be carried out by each pair on the rolls produced by four other groups. Use the Product analysis form on sheet 142 as a starting point for their taste test. Some groups may wish to change the formula of the form. As long as a clear record is kept of who made which roll, it should be possible to come up with the most popular recipes for the bread rolls. Have the most popular ones got common features?

## Suggestion(s) for support

Certain children can be given a more restricted range of 'extra' ingredients. They can also be given more help in determining the feature of the bread rolls they produce (for example, they could add very small pieces of apple to produce a 'fruity' roll for people who want to eat a more healthy diet).

## Assessment opportunities

This activity shows how well children are able to follow a recipe. It also gives an opportunity to assess how well they are able to make changes to an existing recipe to make the end result appeal to certain groups of people. Careful questioning needs to be done to ascertain why the children made certain decisions.

## Opportunities for IT

The children can use a word processor or desktop publishing package to write their own recipe card. They should look at different types of recipes to help them decide how to format their own, possibly using different fonts, styles and sizes, and formatting commands such as centre, tabs or hanging indents. These could be displayed in the classroom or bound to make a class book of bread roll recipes. The children could include pictures scanned from their own line drawings or from photographs of the finished bread rolls.

## Display ideas

Photographs of each roll can be taken. These can be stuck to a card (or scanned into a computer if you have the appropriate IT equipment) and then the children should word process the ingredients and instructions to complete their own recipe card. These can either be displayed on the wall or in the class's own recipe book (as suggested above).

# COCKTAILS                                            FPT

*To use their knowledge of taste and colour to develop an interesting healthy fruit drink.*

†† *Whole class working in groups of four.*

⏱ *Two one-hour sessions.*

⚠ *All the equipment used in this activity should only be used for working with food. Desks should be covered with plastic-coated fabric and cleaned with anti-bacterial spray before the work starts. Children should be reminded of all the food hygiene and safety rules and wash their hands and wear protective clothing. They should be reminded to take care when cutting fruit with sharp knives.*

## Previous skills/knowledge needed

The children will have discussed the features of food products such as colour, taste and texture. They will have worked with some food products in the context of food safety and hygiene rules.

## Key background information

This activity lets the children work with food materials, but without needing access to cooking facilities. It also gives them the opportunity to design a product for a particular market and to have some external evaluation of their work.

**Vocabulary**
Cocktail.

## Preparation

Arrange for a visitor (perhaps the owner of a local restaurant) to come into school to judge the best cocktail. See if they would be prepared to offer a prize of some kind. Have a limited number of pictures of cocktails available for the introductory session. (Not too many, otherwise it will be easy for the children to copy ideas.) Have some different kinds of glasses available (unbreakable if possible).

## Resources needed

Water, soda water, lemonade, milk, fruit juice, ginger beer, apples, oranges, bananas, grapes, lemons, kiwi fruit, cherries, sugar, glasses for the drinks, decorations such as umbrellas or stirrers, plastic table covers, plastic aprons, paper, pencils.

## What to do

Tell the children that they are going to create some fruit drinks which younger children can drink on special occasions. They may have heard of cocktails, and seen drinks with sparklers and umbrellas on television. Each group of four will be given the task of producing a sample of a fruit drink that they think is relatively healthy and that would appeal to younger children. Ask each group to choose a leader to organise the activity.

Talk about the fruits that they could use:

▲ Will the fruit be used for its juice, for its texture, for its colour?

▲ Are some fruits too expensive?

▲ Are some fruits unpopular with most younger children?

▲ What liquids will you use – water, lemonade, soda water, milk, ginger beer?

▲ What sort of glass will you use?

▲ How will you decorate it?

As children come up with ideas, record them in some way so that each group can make reference to them at a later stage. Emphasise the importance of it being a healthy fruit drink and that they should avoid too much sugar or fizzy drinks as a base. The groups should now discuss ideas and come up with at least two possibilities. They should make a sketch of what it will look like, write down suggested names and a list of possible ingredients and instructions.

The proposals are then discussed, and you decide which resources you will provide and which the groups will need to bring in themselves. The list included in 'Resources needed' might be a typical selection that you would be able to provide. Containers and decorations could be borrowed from home or made by the groups themselves.

In the second session, the children having access to all the resources, can make their two drinks and evaluate the one they wish to present. Invite in a visitor who will taste each group's drink and choose the one he or she likes best. It might even be possible for the winning cocktail to be sold at a restaurant for one or two evenings as a prize. Alternatively, the class could sell it in the school canteen at lunch-time.

## Suggestion(s) for extension

The group can produce posters and advertising material for their new fruit cocktail.

## Suggestion(s) for support

An activity of this kind is best done with mixed ability groups. Perhaps the leader of the group could be nominated by the teacher rather than from among the group itself. You could draw up a recipe of a cocktail for the less able children to follow.

## Assessment opportunities

This activity focuses upon group work and on designing a product within certain constraints for a particular market. They have to be able to justify the decisions that they make.

## Opportunities for IT

The children could use an art or drawing package to design an advert or poster for their cocktail.

## Display ideas

Large paintings of the drinks could be made to supplement the 'extension' group's advertising material and then the drinks can be displayed for sale.

# Textiles

This section starts with an investigation into the different kinds of fabric which are to be found in most homes. There are then opportunities to practise sewing techniques, to make and use paper patterns and to learn about a range of techniques suitable for decorating fabric.

These skills can then be developed when the children are involved in design and make activities (see pages 95–104) where there is a need to make use of fabrics. By exploring these techniques at this stage it gives the children a much broader repertoire of skills on which to draw, and ensures that they are actually able to make choices of their own when it comes to decorating the fabric and finishing it appropriately. These activities have been written as focused activities, but most could be easily transformed into design and make activities by giving children much more choice. For example, the children could be asked to make a glove puppet, but the purpose, the character, the type of fabric and the shape, could be decided by the children themselves.

There are obviously close links between art and design and technology in this particular area, and it may be that the techniques could be taught within art sessions and that fabric could be used within a design & technology project.

# FABRICS

*To make children aware of the characteristics of different fabrics.*

**††** *Working in pairs.*

🕐 *1 hour.*

**IDEA**

## Previous skills/knowledge needed

Children will probably have looked at the properties of fabrics before at Key Stage 1. This activity extends their knowledge by introducing the names of different types of fabric and investigating some of their properties.

## Key background information

This activity gives children an opportunity to learn a little about the wide range of fabrics that are available. Textiles are made from fibres which are called natural when they come from animals and plants, and synthetic when they are made from oil. The fibres are twisted together to make yarns.

The yarn is then turned into fabric by either weaving or knitting. Woven fabric tends not to stretch, whereas knitted fabric does. (Try stretching the material of a jacket [woven] and compare it with stretching the material of a pullover [knitted].)

Natural fibres such as wool (from sheep), silk (from the cocoons of silk worms), cotton and linen (from cotton and flax plants) and synthetic fibres such as nylon, polyester, viscose and Lycra are often mixed together to form yarns which have particular enhanced properties. An obvious example is the combination of cotton with Lycra for 'exercise' clothing. The cotton has good absorbency to cope with perspiration and the Lycra gives the fabric some elasticity making sure that it keeps its shape during energetic exercise. Similarly, mixtures of wool and nylon provide a more hard-wearing fabric with the overall softness of wool, and a mixture of polyester and cotton has the coolness of cotton but is much easier to wash and iron than pure cotton.

## Vocabulary

Woven, synthetic, knitted, yarns, cocoon, flax, linen, Lycra, viscose, polyester, fibre.

Some of the names of fabrics are complex and may cause problems for some children. Make sure that they realise the purpose of the activity and do not get tied up over trying to spell certain words.

## Preparation

Prepare a large table with the headings 'Type of article' and 'Type of fabric' for class results to be recorded. You will need to ask the children to do some research at home prior to the start of this lesson. Ask them to copy down the information that they find on the labels of five fabrics at home. These can include curtains and towels as well as clothing. You can be quite prescriptive – just ask them to write down what the fabric is made of, or ask that they include as much information as possible from the labels, including manufacturer, washing instructions, as this can be used in an extension activity.

You need a few examples of clothes labels for the introductory session. Label small samples of a large selection of different fabrics with their names and words that can be used to describe them, for example, silk might be shiny and smooth, cotton might be soft.

## Resources needed

Some clothes with their labels to use in the introduction, a collection of labelled fabric samples, photocopiable sheet 144 for each child, writing materials, a large version of the photocopiable sheet, books, photographs and videos of natural and synthetic materials.

## What to do

Discuss information that can be found on fabric labels, using the examples you have brought in for this introduction. Ask children to get out the information they have written down about the five fabrics they found in their home. Now arrange a class discussion on what they have discovered. Record some of the results on the table you have prepared. A number of questions are likely to arise – Why are things made out of different fabrics? Why are fabrics made out of a mixture of yarns? It is important for children to realise that if the label on a shirt says '55% Cotton 45% Polyester' it does not mean that part of the shirt is made out of cotton, and another part is made out of polyester. It means that some cotton yarn and some polyester yarn have been twisted tightly together to make one mixture. As the discussion continues provide some information on natural and synthetic materials (see 'Key background information') with appropriate use of books, photographs, slides and videos.

Now discuss the properties of different fabrics. Give each pair a sample with its name and properties on a label. Ask them to think of other words that could describe the fabric. Get the children to fill in the table on photocopiable sheet 144. Now swap the samples around and encourage the children to extend the table with more descriptive words which

**DESIGN AND TECHNOLOGY**

can be used to describe fabrics – it does not have to be limited to one word for each fabric as some have similar properties. Do not forget the colour or the pattern of the fabric.

Discuss the words in the table as a whole class. To finish off this work, take all the labels off the fabrics. Get a child to think of one of the fabrics and then get the rest of the class to ask questions about its properties which can be answered 'yes' or 'no'. See how quickly children can guess which fabric was selected.

### Suggestion(s) for extension
Children could make up their own guessing game using their knowledge of materials. They could also look at the benefits of using mixtures of fibres rather than just one.

### Suggestion(s) for support
Some children may require more one-to-one support when they are investigating the properties of the material samples.

### Assessment opportunities
Completion of the table will show a basic understanding of the characteristics of different fabrics.

### Opportunities for IT
The children could use a computer database to record the information they have discovered about the various fabrics. Discuss with the class how the database should be set up in order to make it useful and able to cope with the wide range of information.

Some useful fieldnames might include:

| | |
|---|---|
| use | *shirt* |
| fabric name | *none* |
| content 1 | *cotton* |
| content 2 | *polyester* |
| content 3 | *–* |
| washing | *40°C* |
| tumble dry | *yes* |
| iron | *cool* |
| manufacture | *woven* |
| properties | *easy to wash* |

The list of headings could be extended or reduced depending on the age and experience of the children. The information could be used to answer questions like:
▲ How many fabrics contain more than one fibre?
▲ Which fabrics can be washed at 40°C?
▲ How many fabrics contain cotton?
▲ Which order would you iron fabrics in? (Perhaps they would sort using temperature as the variable.)

The children could also use a branching database to create an electronic key for identifying the different fabrics. This type of database differs from conventional ones in that the children must teach the software about the different fabrics

by phrasing questions that can only be answered with a 'yes' or 'no'. Answering 'yes' to a question leads in one direction, 'no' in another. This skill makes the task a good language activity as well.

For example, asking the question:

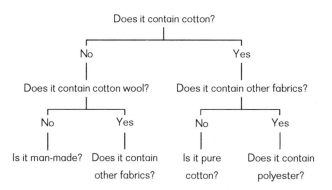

The activity is best organised in small groups with a limited range of fabrics to start with. A key part of the activity is to decide on the first question which will provide a good basis for splitting the whole set of fabrics into two fairly equal parts.

### Display ideas
Get the children to produce enlarged labels from clothing either by hand, or on a computer. Put the garment on the display board together with the enlarged labels. Words describing the properties of the fabrics can then be fixed to the appropriate garments.

### Reference to photocopiable sheet
Sheet 144 gives a table to describe fabrics, together with some examples.

DESIGN AND
TECHNOLOGY

# A BOOKMARK  FPT

*To practise a range of stitches. To design a*
*simple cross-stitch bookmark.*

**††** *Working individually.*

🕐 *Three one-hour sessions.*

⚠ *Warn children of the dangers of using sharp needles.*

### Previous skills/knowledge needed

The children will be aware of a number of different stitches
from their Key Stage 1 textiles work. This activity builds upon
that experience.

### Key background information

This activity gives children practise in using a number of stitches
and allows them to make a simple bookmark of their own. As
they are using Binca the techniques will be easier to practise.

### Vocabulary

Running stitch, back stitch, open satin stitch, chain stitch,
buttonhole stitch, embroidery, laced running stitch, stem
stitch, satin stitch, lazy daisy stitch, cross-stitch, Binca.

### Preparation

You should prepare an A4 sheet with a large diagram of
each stitch at the top clearly labelled, and a sample of each
stitch in fabric stuck on the bottom of the sheet. These can
be displayed on the wall after the introductory session. You
will need to cut up pieces of Binca about 5cm by 10cm for
each child in the class. You will also need an example design
including a name and a small image illustrating an interest.

### Resources needed

Binca cut into the shape for a bookmark, large needles,
embroidery thread in a wide range of colours, one copy of
photocopiable sheet 145 for each child, pencils.

### What to do

Remind the children of the stitches which they have done
previously. Get them to look at stitches in their own clothing
and point out that there are many ways in which thread or
cotton can be used to hold pieces of fabric together. Explain
that it is possible to use stitches to add patterns or pictures
to fabric and that this is called embroidery. Tell them that in
order to practise some stitches they are going to embroider
a small bookmark.

Show them the samples of the stitches on your prepared
A4 sheet, and demonstrate them on a spare piece of Binca.
Start with the relatively simple ones. Depending on the
experience of the class, introduce them to a range of new
stitches. Some of the more complex ones you may decide
to give to an able group as an extension exercise.

Explain to the children that their bookmark should have
their name on and also a small picture which represents one

of their interests. Explain how the picture should be quite
simple – a book for a person who enjoys reading, a paw
mark for someone with a cat or dog as a pet, or a horseshoe
for someone who likes riding. Show them how to create their
design by shading in the squares on the grid on photocopiable
sheet 145 (a sample design is shown on the sheet). Cross-
stitch should be used for the majority of the design although
other stitches can be used for particular effects. When the
children have completed their designs on paper they can be
checked, and alternative stitches suggested if necessary. Then
the children can embroider their design.

### Suggestion(s) for extension

Children who are competent at sewing can be encouraged
to include as many different stitches in their design as
possible. Perhaps there could be a prize for the person who
includes the largest number of different stitches in a quality
piece of work.

### Suggestion(s) for support

The children can be given help with the original design of
their name, and a relatively simple picture could be selected
for them. They should also be asked to concentrate on only
one or two different stitches.

### Assessment opportunities

The quality of the finished bookmark, and the complexity of
the stitching will provide a good indication of how competent
the child is at using stitches.

### Opportunities for IT

The children could use a drawing package to help them design
their bookmark. If the background grid is turned on and the
grid size set to 0.5cm or less (so that the full size of the
Binca bookmark is displayed on the screen) the children can
fill in the different squares to create their design. They can
add colour and use different line thicknesses or other symbols
to denote the different kinds of stitch to be used. The
completed design can be printed out and used as a pattern
for the children's own embroidery.

**DESIGN AND
TECHNOLOGY**

## Display ideas

The most effective display of these products would be in their permanent use in the children's reading books in the classroom. However, they could be wall mounted together with their original designs, and the large, labelled sample stitches which were used in the introduction.

## Reference to photocopiable sheet

Sheet 145 shows samples of stitches, a blank grid for designing their own bookmark and a sample design.

Stitches and bookmark design

---

## A TIE-DYED BAG — FPT

*To learn and develop the techniques involved in tie-dying. To use sewing skills to make a small bag.*

†† *Working in pairs.*

⏱ *Three one-hour sessions.*

⚠ *Use plastic gloves and protective overalls. Remind children to take care when using pins and needles.*

## Previous skills/knowledge needed

Children will have sewn fabric together using a range of stitches. They will be familiar with the idea of making a paper pattern.

## Key background information

This is an ancient technique which can be used to produce interesting and quite complicated patterns. Basically, before being immersed in dye, part of the fabric is tied tightly to prevent dye getting to it. When the fabric is untied, the pattern can be seen. The fabric produced can be used for anything, but in this activity it is suggested that it is made into a small bag.

## Vocabulary

Tie and dye.

## Preparation

You will need to prepare some samples of tie-dyed fabric using different 'tying' techniques. You will also need to have separate pieces of an unmade bag and to make a completed bag out of some of the fabric as shown in Figure 7.1. Make up the cold-water dye according to the instructions on the packet. If the children will want to wash their fabric, make sure that you add a fixing agent to the dye at this stage. It is probably better to have one or two large containers of dye for the children to use rather than lots of small ones on each desk.

## Resources needed

The cold-water dye solution, scissors, pins, needles, thread, plastic gloves, washing-up liquid, overalls, newspapers, cotton fabric (30cm square for each child), paper, writing materials, sample bag, copy of photocopiable sheet 146 for each child. Optional: pebbles, Plasticine, string, pipe cleaners.

## What to do

Show the children a sample of fabric which has been decorated using tie-dying. Explain how to tie a piece of cotton fabric in a variety of ways to obtain different patterns. Show them how to get different effects using string, pegs, elastic bands, stones and lumps of Plasticine.

Give each child a copy of photocopiable sheet 146 which illustrates how to produce some tie-dye effects. Tell them that they are going to make a small bag out of their dyed fabric. The children should choose the technique they wish to use and tie-dye their fabric following the instructions on photocopiable sheet 146. Now show them the sample bag, and the unfinished separate pieces. Explain how they should draw a pattern on some paper, pin the pattern to the fabric and cut out the two pieces. They can then pin and sew them right sides together, hem the top, turn the bag 'inside out' and add handles.

The children can decide on their purpose for their particular bag, although the dimensions should be kept reasonably small to avoid using too many resources.

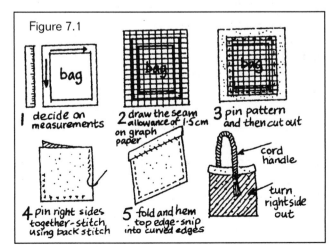

Figure 7.1

1 decide on measurements

2 draw the seam allowance of 1·5cm on graph paper

3 pin pattern and then cut out

4 pin right sides together- stitch using back stitch

5 fold and hem top edge- snip into curved edges

cord handle

turn right side out

The process of tie-dying

▲ Put on your protective overall and plastic gloves.

▲ Take your piece of material, roll it up and then tie some knots in it.

▲ Put the fabric into the dye solution and stir it for ten minutes

▲ Leave for another ten minutes.

▲ Rinse the fabric in water with a little drop of washing-up liquid.

▲ Put it under the cold water tap to rinse.

▲ Untie the knots, and iron it flat while it is still damp.

▲ You can experiment with other patterns by tying the material in different ways.

## Suggestion(s) for extension
Children can decorate the bag further using other techniques, such as using fabric paint. Alternatively, children could make more sophisticated patterns by tie-dying the fabric again using a different technique, and a different-coloured dye.

## Suggestion(s) for support
The paper pattern for the bag could already be provided, or the pieces of material could be cut out ready for the children to sew them together.

## Assessment opportunities
The tie-dyed pattern which is obtained gives some idea of the way in which children undertook the process, for example, if the pattern is very faint then the idea of tying the knots very tight was not fully appreciated. The quality of the finished bag gives an opportunity to assess the children's sewing and finishing skills.

## Display ideas
The display can consist of a piece of material tied up in a particular way next to an opened-up piece of fabric showing the sort of pattern which it produces. Additionally, a range of the bags could be included next to some cotton fabric to show the way in which a piece of cotton material can be transformed into a finished product.

## Reference to photocopiable sheet
Sheet 146 explains the process of tie-dying fabric, and shows some 'tying' techniques.

## A BATIK PLACE MAT — FPT
*To learn and develop the techniques involved in batik. To design a pattern which would be suitable to use as a place mat.*

†† *Working individually. (This activity should be done with a small group of children under close adult supervision, ideally by a classroom assistant.)*

*Three one-hour sessions.*

⚠ *The wax must be melted in a thermostatically-controlled batik pot. Children should wear plastic gloves and protective overalls. They should be warned of the dangers of using hot wax and how they can receive nasty burns from an electric iron.*

### Previous skills/knowledge needed
They should have decorated fabrics in other ways, such as using fabric paints, and will be aware of the basic process of using coloured dye with material.

### Key background information
Batik is a method of dying fabric, using wax to limit where the dye actually makes contact with the fabric. The activity should not be done as a whole class, as close supervision is required because of the dangers associated with the hot wax and an electric iron. However, the children should be heavily involved in the activity and the adult assistant should be made aware of this.

### Vocabulary
Batik, thermostatically-controlled, tjanting.

DESIGN AND TECHNOLOGY

## Preparation

The wax should be melted in a thermostatically-controlled batik pot. Make up the cold-water dye according to the instructions on the packet. If the children will want to wash their fabric, make sure that you add a fixing agent to the dye at this stage. Provide one or two large containers of dye for the children to use rather than lots of small ones on each desk. Some samples of batik work should be available for the children to look at.

## Resources needed

Batik sample, a piece of plain cotton fabric (20cm × 30cm) for each child, thermostatically-controlled batik pot, paraffin wax, old paintbrushes (you will not be able to use them for anything else but batik work) or a tjanting (traditional implement), cold-water dyes, large plastic containers, newspaper, white paper, electric iron, one copy of photocopiable sheet 147 for each child.

The process of batik

❶ Draw your design on paper and when you are happy with it go over it in black felt-tipped pen

❷ Put your white fabric over the top of your design and clip the paper to it.

❸ Decide which parts of your design you wish to remain white and carefully cover these parts with melted wax.

❹ When the wax is cool add the fabric to your first chosen colour dye. You must use the lightest colour first. Then let the fabric dry

❺ Decide which parts of the design are going to stay this colour. Cover these with more hot wax. Put the fabric into dye of the second colour. Again let the fabric dry. Repeat this process until your design is complete.

❻ Now you can remove the wax by putting the fabric between sheets of newspaper and using a hot iron. Put a sheet of plain paper between the fabric and the newspaper to stop ink stains spoiling your work. Keep changing the newspaper and plain paper until all the wax has disappeared.

## What to do

Show the children a sample of fabric which has been decorated using batik. Tell the children that they are going to use the same technique to make a place mat to give to someone as a present. This will give the children a focus for their design. Give the children a copy of photocopiable sheet 147 and ask them to follow the instructions while you simultaneously demonstrate the process they need to go through.

Draw a design on paper and then go over it in black felt-tipped pen. Emphasise that the children's designs should not be too complex – simple patterns are often the most effective. Put a piece of white fabric over the top of the design (the black pen should show through) and clip the paper and

the fabric together. Decide which parts of your design you wish to remain white and carefully cover them with melted wax. Use either an old paintbrush or, if you have one available, show them a tjanting which is the traditional implement used in batik work. The wax is kept hot in the round metal sphere and it flows down the pointed spout rather like ink in a pen. The wax must be hot enough to soak right into the fabric. Emphasise the importance of safety when using the brushes and the hot wax.

When the wax is cool add the fabric to your first chosen colour dye. You must use the lightest colour first. (If you use a dark dye first then subsequent lighter dyes will not cover up the first colour.) Then let the fabric dry. (Do not be tempted to dry it more quickly on a radiator – the wax will melt!) Decide which parts of the design are going to stay this colour and then cover these with more hot wax. Now put the fabric into dye of the second colour. Again let the fabric dry. Keep repeating this process until your design is complete.

Show the children how to remove the wax by putting the fabric between sheets of newspaper and using a hot iron. Put a sheet of plain paper between the fabric and the newspaper to stop ink stains spoiling your work. The wax melts and soaks into the newspaper. Keep changing the newspaper and plain paper until all the wax has disappeared from the fabric.

## Suggestion(s) for extension

More intricate patterns and images can be achieved by repeating the process, each time using a different colour of dye. The children could choose their own item to make using the batik technique.

## Suggestion(s) for support

Some children may be encouraged to produce extremely simple designs (or have them done for them) and to undertake the dying process once only. Interesting results can still be achieved.

## Assessment opportunities

The quality of the finished product will give you an opportunity to assess how accurately the wax has been painted onto the fabric. The intricacy of the piece of work also provides a measure of the children's design capability.

## Display ideas

The use of the place mats at lunch-time will provide an opportunity for the class's work to be displayed. They could also be used on the refreshments table at parents' or governors' meetings and at fund-raising events in the school.

## Reference to photocopiable sheet

Sheet 147 goes through the basic process of batik. It is written in a very general way so that it forms a useful reference whenever children wish to use this technique.

**DESIGN AND TECHNOLOGY**

## A GLOVE PUPPET    FPT

*To select a character for their glove puppet
using brainstorming. To practise skills of sewing and
using a pattern and fabric paints.*

**††** *Working in groups of four and then individually.*

🕐 *Three one-hour sessions.*

**⚠** *Remind children that pins and needles are sharp
and should be used with care.*

### Previous skills/knowledge needed
Children should have done some sewing and be familiar with
using fabric paints.

### Key background information
This activity uses a very basic-shaped glove puppet with the
face being an integral part of the textile work. The focus is
on producing a pattern and decorating the glove puppet to
their chosen design using fabric paints. The contexts in which
an activity of this kind could be undertaken are extremely
varied. The activity could be done in groups with each one
producing characters for a particular puppet play linked to a
topic which the children are covering. Alternatively, the
activity could be organised as below, so that each individual
child makes a puppet of their own for themselves or a
younger brother or sister.

### Vocabulary
Pattern, brainstorming.

### Preparation
You should have one basic glove puppet shape completed
without decoration and one with.

### Resources needed
Felt, scissors, needle, thread, beads, buttons, wool, fabric
paints and crayons, paper, pens, blank and decorated glove
puppet shapes as examples, one copy of photocopiable sheet
148 for each child.

### What to do
Tell the children that they are going to make a glove puppet
for themselves or as a gift for a younger brother or sister. In
groups of four get them to brainstorm ideas for characters,
either specific or generic. (Remind children that in brainstorming
they should say whatever comes into their minds, and no one
should criticise it for being silly! Only when the group has a
large list of ideas are they ready to discuss them.)

Bring the groups together and discuss the ideas. The
purpose of this is to widen the choice for children who may
have been able to think of only one or two ideas. Emphasise
that each child can make whatever character they like – it is
not a matter of stealing ideas from someone else, but when
designing and making it is important to get ideas from as
many sources as possible.

Show the children the basic glove shape that they will
make and one which has been decorated. Ask each child to
draw out their ideas using the basic shape shown below.

Give each child a copy of photocopiable sheet 148 and
go through the following procedures for making the pattern:
making a mock-up, cutting the fabric, sewing the fabric and
using the fabric paints to complete the puppet. It is suggested
that on this occasion you use felt as it avoids the necessity
for hemming the edges, and it provides a basic colour on
which the rest of the design can be built. Ask children to
consider carefully which colour felt they will use.

The procedure is:

▲ Draw round your hand onto paper (to make sure the
puppet fits you) and then make a glove puppet shape around
the outline. If the basic shape is to be altered (to include a
witch's hat or some large ears, for example) it should be
done at this stage.

▲ Draw a line about 1cm from the puppet outline – when
you sew round the edge of the material you cannot sew
right at the very edge – this is called seam allowance.

▲ Cut the pattern out, and draw round it onto two sheets of
paper. Join the two paper cut-outs together using staples
around the edge – if this is done properly, the pieces of fabric
will be sewn together along this line.

▲ Put it on your hand to check the size. Roughly draw some
features and clothes onto the mock-up using felt-tipped pen.

**DESIGN AND
TECHNOLOGY**

**Making a glove puppet**

▲ Draw round your hand on a piece of paper.

▲ Now draw a basic glove puppet shape around your hand outline.

▲ Make any changes you want to at this stage. Draw another line about 1cm from outside your first outline. When you sew round the edge of the material you cannot sew right ot the very edge – you need to sew about 1cm in. (This is called the seam allowance.)

▲ Cut your pattern out, and draw round it onto two sheets of paper. Keep your pattern safe.

▲ Now join the two paper cut-outs together using staples around the edge

▲ Put it carefully on your hand. Is it the right size? Roughly draw some features and clothes onto the mock-up.

▲ Go on to make your glove puppet out of fabric.

▲ Use your pattern to make two copies in paper. Pin the patterns onto the fabric.

▲ Cut out the two pieces of fabric. Take the patterns off. and pin the two pieces together.

▲ Sew all the way round about 1cm from the edge of the puppet except the bottom edge where you will need to put your hand!

▲ Cut little nicks into the seam allowance, but no further, on all the curves.

▲ Turn the puppet inside out and ask your teacher to press it with an iron.

▲ Now, using fabric paints and things like beads, buttons and wool, decorate your glove puppet so that it looks like your chosen character.

Then make the puppet out of fabric if you are happy with the idea – otherwise make another pattern and mock-up.

▲ Use your basic shape pattern to make two copies in paper – one for the front and one for the back. Pin these to the fabric. They should be as close as possible so you do not waste any fabric.

▲ Cut out the two pieces of fabric. Take the patterns off and pin the fabric together. This will keep it in place while it is being sewn. Sew round the edge of the puppet, using a sewing machine if you have one, *but do not sew the bottom edge which is where you need to put your hand!* Sew about 1cm from the edge – provided by the extra bit added on the first drawing. Cut little nicks into the seam allowance, *but no further,* on all the curves. This will help as you turn the puppet inside out.

▲ Press your puppet with an iron and using fabric paints and beads, buttons and wool, decorate the glove puppet.

They should look at their original design and finished product and write down the similarities and differences, and how and why they occurred. They can write down three positive and three negative features of their glove puppet.

## Suggestion(s) for extension

Children could have a wider choice of fabric, an opportunity to change the pattern more extensively (there are many books available with patterns for glove puppets which would provide stimuli), or make a head out of papier mâché to add to the fabric body. They could also be encouraged to seek evaluative comments about their work from others in the group.

## Suggestion(s) for support

Children should have the sample glove shape to help them, or additionally be given the finished product which they use to develop their own designs.

## Assessment opportunities

This activity can be used to see how well children produce a pattern, the standard of the children's sewing and how they evaluate their finished product.

## Opportunities for IT

The children could use a drawing program to create their own glove puppet pattern. If the background grid is turned on, it will help children to create symmetrical patterns for the puppet so that the two sides match. The pattern could be printed, cut out and used by the children. They may need to use the software's enlargement facility to make their original design fit an A4 sheet of paper.

## Display ideas

The children's original design and the finished puppet should be displayed side by side with a few sentences from each child commenting on the similarities and differences between the two.

## Reference to photocopiable sheet

Sheet 148 goes through the basic procedures that the children need to follow when making their glove puppet. The term 'fabric' is used throughout rather than 'felt' in case you decide to experiment with other materials.

## A HAIRY HEDGEHOG  ◆FPT◆

*To enable children to practise using patterns.*
*To develop and practise their sewing techniques.*

†† *Working individually. (This activity should probably be undertaken by a small group of children at a time, especially if they are going to use a sewing machine.)*

🕐 *Three one-hour sessions.*

⚠ *Children should be warned to be careful when using pins and needles. Individual tuition should be given if children are to use electric sewing machines. Children should be aware of the importance of using safety eyes and noses for their soft toys.*

## Previous skills/knowledge needed

Children should be familiar with using paper patterns and should have practised basic sewing techniques.

## Key background information

This activity is intended to develop the children's skills in working with fabric, using patterns, putting the component pieces together, sewing, stuffing and finishing. There is little opportunity for the children's own designs. This is an ideal opportunity in which to introduce the use of a sewing machine. Once children have completed an activity of this kind they should have the basic skills to produce soft toys from other patterns and subsequently to develop patterns for their own designs. This activity requires considerable perseverance from the children, and should be contemplated only with those who have had the opportunity to develop their skills of working with textiles in a range of other activities.

## Vocabulary
Pattern, pinning, ladder stitch.

## Preparation
You should have one of the hedgehogs already completed. Ideally, it should be a large one in order to achieve maximum impact during the introductory session. By using the variable enlargement facility on a photocopier it is possible to create patterns for hedgehogs of various sizes from photocopiable sheet 149. The size you select will be a compromise between the cost of the materials and the appeal of a large hedgehog!

## Resources needed
Fur fabric, felt, safety noses, safety eyes, scraps of other materials for additional clothing and accessories, needles, sewing thread, sewing machine, stuffing material such as old tights, foam or wadding, one copy of photocopiable sheet 149 for each child.

## What to do
If children are going to use a sewing machine, this activity should be done in a small group with adult supervision. Remind the helper that they should assist, but not make the hedgehog for the children. Show the children the large hedgehog, and explain to them that they are going to use a pattern to make their own soft toy for a younger child who is a relation, a friend or perhaps someone in the infant or nursery classes. Then demonstrate how to make one.

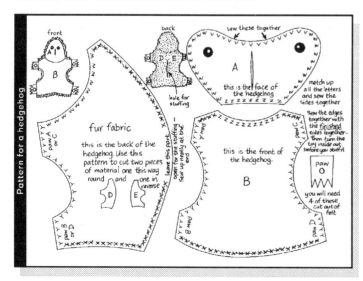

Remind the children how to cut out the paper pattern, pin it to the appropriate type and colour of material, cut out the material and pin the finished sides together. Show them how to use the sewing machine to sew all the way round the body, leaving a small gap. Turn the toy inside out, and fix the safety eyes and nose. Take this opportunity to talk about the importance of these devices rather than sewing on buttons.

Stuff the toy with appropriate soft material and then neatly sew up the gap by hand using a ladder stitch (see Figure 7.2). Now give out photocopiable sheet 149 and let the children make their own hedgehog using the same procedure.

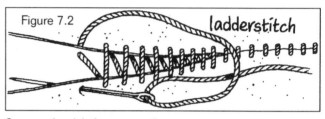

Figure 7.2    ladderstitch

## Suggestion(s) for extension
Clothes and accessories could be made for the hedgehog family along the lines of the many collections of toy animal families which can be found in gift shops and craft fairs.

## Suggestion(s) for support
Individuals may need help when sewing and pinning the pattern together. As suggested above, this activity would benefit from a classroom assistant, who can offer a great deal of support to some children.

## Assessment opportunities
A good quality model will provide evidence that the children have considerable skill in techniques associated with work with fabric. As this should be done as a small group activity, there will be opportunities to observe and assess the children's ability concerning very specific aspects of the process such as sewing skills, use of a pattern and overall dexterity.

### Display ideas
A table and wall display area can be decorated as a woodland scene and all the hedgehogs produced by the class put onto the table or in a tree house, together with name labels round their necks. As an end of term activity, you could arrange for a treasure hunt, where cryptic clues are given leading to which hedgehog is hiding the 'treasure'. At the end of the day one person can be given the opportunity to go to the display, pick up the hedgehog and see if they were right!

### Reference to photocopiable sheet
Sheet 149 contains a pattern for a relatively small hedgehog, together with some instructions reminding children of the order in which they need to carry out each task. The sheets can be copied in different sizes depending on how large you want the hedgehog to be.

# Electricity

In this section children will have the opportunity to design and make electrical circuits which are incorporated into their products, as well as gain knowledge and understand about a range of simple switches and other electrical components such as motors and buzzers. The activities build upon the work they will have covered in science, but focus upon the skills and techniques which are required in order to integrate electrical circuits into their models.

Children start by looking at a wide range of existing switches and then make some of their own. They can evaluate existing electrical products in the form of torches, and identify some of the design decisions which would have taken place. The focused practical tasks develop skills of soldering and circuit design. They can take these ideas further with more complex models incorporating a range of different switches, motors and buzzers.

Work on this topic can enhance designing and making in many contexts but transport, the fairground and stories are particularly useful as foci for these activities.

DESIGN AND
TECHNOLOGY

# EVALUATING TORCHES ◆ IDEA

*To disassemble torches to help find out how they*
*work. To draw an exploded annotated diagram.*
*To practise drawing techniques.*

†† *Working individually.*

🕐 *Two one-hour sessions.*

## Previous skills/knowledge needed

Children will need to have covered some basic circuit work in science. They should understand that a complete metal path is needed for electricity to flow. They will also have covered some basic drawing skills.

## Key background information

This activity gives children an opportunity to look closely at an existing product with which they will be familar – an electric torch – and to discuss why it was designed in the way it is. It also provides an opportunity to develop further graphic skills and to create links with art.

## Vocabulary

Torch, exploded, annotated.

## Preparation

Ask each child to bring into school a torch from home. Put them on a display table with each torch labelled with its owner's name. Children can be encouraged to look at them, but not touch, prior to the lesson.

## Resources needed

Large selection of different types of torches, drawing paper, paper, pens, coloured crayons, felt-tipped pens, aqua pencils, a copy of photocopiable sheet 150 for support.

## What to do

Start the session off as a whole class. Hold up a number of the torches and encourage discussion about them. This activity gives an opportunity to consider evaluation of particular aspects of the product.

Consider appearance first:

▲ Why is it the shape it is?

▲ Does the handle have to be that long in order to hold it or is it because it needs a space to hold the batteries?

▲ What do you think about the colour scheme?

▲ Are the colours chosen for a particular reason, for example, so you can see it more easily in the dark?

Next discuss its function:

▲ Does it provide light in the dark?

▲ Could it be brighter?

▲ Does it need to be bigger if it is to give a brighter light?

▲ Why has it got a sliding switch and/or a push switch?

▲ Has it got more than one light source?

▲ Does one of them flash? If so, why?

Safety is another important aspect:

▲ Is it battery powered or mains powered? Why?

▲ What material is it made from? Why?

▲ If it breaks is it likely to harm you in any way?

Finally, you could discuss the importance of its reliability:

▲ Is it important that it works when you want it to?

▲ What might happen if it didn't?

▲ The batteries in torches always seem to be run down when you need them! Do any of the torches try to solve this problem? What could you do to solve the problem?

In this class discussion you should be bringing out how important it is to think in a great deal of detail about the design of any product. Now give every child a torch. Ask them to take it to pieces carefully. Emphasise that they should only undo things that are meant to be undone. In the case of a torch, this will mean removing parts necessary for the replacement of the batteries and the bulb. If you make sure that children disassemble their own torches then they are likely to be more inclined to be careful, and make sure that they put them back together again.

Ask them to work out what each piece is made of and to think why that material was chosen. Remind them of the work they have done in science on circuits. Electricity needs a complete metal path in order for it to flow. Try to work out the complete path inside the torch. Ask each child to produce a large drawing of their torch showing the different pieces and how they fit together. Tell them that this is called an *exploded diagram*. They should also write onto their drawing paper all the things that they have found out about the torch, such as what it is made of, why it is made of that material, why the colour was chosen and where the electricity flows. These extra comments are called *annotations*. Emphasise how detailed these comments should be (for example: if

**DESIGN AND TECHNOLOGY**

made from black rubber – rubber is used so that it is difficult to break as a torch could easily be dropped, and the torch is black because it is likely to be used in messy places, and the dirt will not show up easily).

## Suggestion(s) for extension
Children could be taught how to use colour and shading to produce higher quality presentation drawings.

## Suggestion(s) for support
Children who are having difficulty with a 3-D drawing could be asked to do a much simpler picture or sketch of the torch. There could also be much less emphasis on the exploded nature of the drawing. Photocopiable sheet 150 gives them an example of the sort of drawing you are expecting and could be used to support the less able children.

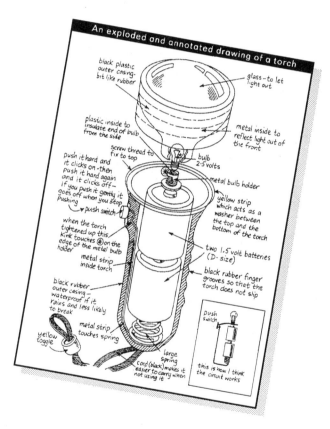

## Assessment opportunities
This activity gives children an opportunity to show how well they can produce an exploded and annotated drawing. In particular look for the detail in the annotations. If they are done effectively they will show their level of understanding both of the way the torch functions and of its design.

## Opportunities for IT
The children could use a drawing or CAD package to draw exploded and labelled diagrams of their torches. It will be helpful to use a background grid and 'snap to grid' option to help children with their drawings.

## Display ideas
The exploded and annotated drawings are displayed next to the actual torch. It is best if the torches can be fixed to the display boards using Velcro or a home-made cardboard holder or bracket.

## Reference to photocopiable sheet
Sheet 150 shows a typical exploded and annotated drawing of a torch and is to be used as support material.

---

# SWITCHES
### IDEA

***To develop children's knowledge of switches and learn how to make some simple home-made ones.***

†† *Working in groups of four and then pairs.*

⏱ *Two one-hour sessions.*

⚠ *For work on these investigations use dry batteries only. Rechargeable batteries should be avoided in situations where children could create a short-circuit.*

## Previous skills/knowledge needed
Children will need to have covered some basic circuit work in science. They should know that a break in the circuit stops electricity from flowing.

## Key background information
In this activity children will investigate a wide range of different switches and learn about their properties. All switches stop electricity from flowing in a circuit, but they do it under different conditions, and alternative switches need to be used in different applications. There are also times when simple switches can be made and incorporated into models. This activity looks at both commercially available and home-made switches and provides information useful to many other activities.

## Vocabulary
Toggle switch, rocker switch, push-to-break switch, push-to-make switch, reed switch, micro switch.

## Preparation
Each group of four children should have a full range of switches and a testing rig. The rig should consist of batteries, battery holder and battery clip, one light-emitting diode (LED), wire and two crocodile clips connected together in a series circuit (see diagram below). This will allow children to test each switch in turn to discover its properties.

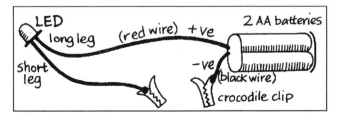

**DESIGN AND TECHNOLOGY**

## Suggestion(s) for extension

Each group can be given one particular type of switch to focus on. They then try to find as many situations as possible where that type of switch is used. Electrical catalogues and looking at electrical appliances at home and at school are useful sources of reference. They should draw a sketch of each application. Children could also be asked to devise other ways of making certain switches other than the methods shown on photocopiable sheet 152.

## Suggestion(s) for support

The use of differentiated photocopiable sheets as described in the 'Reference to photocopiable sheets' section below will help children at different levels of ability.

## Assessment opportunities

The successful completion of photocopiable sheet 151 will show a basic understanding of a range of switches. The level of this understanding will depend on how much assistance the particular graded sheet gives to the children.

## Display ideas

The display could consist of each group's chosen switch, together with information about how it works and the sketches of the places where they would be found.

## Resources needed

A selection of different switches including a push switch, a slide switch, a toggle or rocker switch, a push-to-make switch, a push-to-break switch, a reed switch and magnet, a tilt switch and a micro switch; brass paper fasteners, multi-strand wire, paper-clips, drawing pins, small blocks of wood, plastic film canisters, ball bearings, aluminium foil, marbles, cardboard, a switch testing rig (see 'Preparation' above), a copy of photocopiable sheet 151 for each child, copies of photocopiable sheet 152 per pair, books on switches, electrical catalogues, CD-ROM encyclopaedia.

## What to do

Revise work on electric circuits that will have been done in science. Remind the children that a switch turns the flow of electricity on and off. Demonstrate the use of the testing rig by joining the two crocodile clips onto each of the terminals of a toggle switch. The LED lights up when the toggle switch is flicked. In groups of four, and using one of the versions of photocopiable sheet 151 you have prepared (see 'Reference to photocopiable sheets'), they should investigate the properties of the different switches. They should complete photocopiable sheet 151 as they progress through the work.

Each group should then split into pairs and build some of the switches shown on photocopiable sheet 152. Again they can experiment with them using the testing rig.

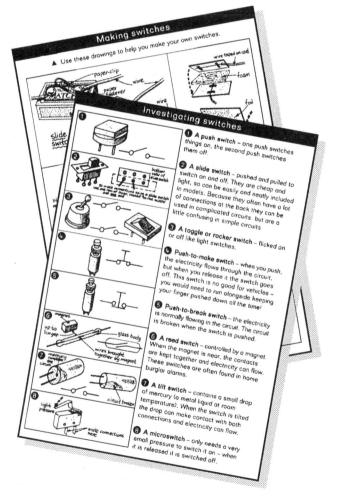

### Reference to photocopiable sheets

Sheet 151 shows the range of switches which are available and gives some background information on them. It can be used in two different ways. As it stands it can provide support for children who are having difficulty with the activity. However, if after you have produced the first set of photocopies, you delete some of the words in the descriptions of the various switches, the sheet then provides a structure for the activity, but requires more input from the children. (Using this approach you can create infinitely variable sheets – just leave the headings and the diagrams for the most able group, use a traditional cloze procedure [deleting every tenth word] for the next group and delete some relatively 'easy' words for the next and so on.) Sheet 152 shows how to make some home-made switches, such as, slide and press switches.

---

### ◆ AN ENTERTAINING DISPLAY ◆ FPT

*To use simple electrical switches and circuits to make a display which will light up. To introduce children to the technique of soldering.*

**††** *Working individually or in pairs.*

**🕐** *Four one-hour sessions.*

**⚠** *Children should be reminded to take care when using a craft knife and soldering iron. They should also use a metal safety rule and cutting mat.*

---

### Previous skills/knowledge needed

Children should have covered basic electric circuits in science. They should also be aware of switches and how they are used. Ideally they will have completed the 'Switches' activity on page 79.

### Key background information

This activity gives children an opportunity to learn about light-emitting diodes (LEDs) and how they can be joined together. Large LEDs which can be bought from educational suppliers have a number of advantages over bulbs. They do not need a special holder, as bulbs do, and they also come in a range of colours (red, green and yellow typically). They only require a very small electric current, which means that batteries run down much less quickly than when using bulbs. They are also quite neat, and can be incorporated into models easily. If you purchase them from educational suppliers, you will find that they work with a wide range of voltages. (Beware if you purchase from electronics suppliers. You will find you have to be much more careful and will need to connect a resistor in series with the LED to prevent damage.)

Disadvantages to using LEDs are that they have to be connected the right way round in the circuit (long leg of LED must be connected, eventually, to the + of the battery) and they need to be soldered into the circuit. This activity, therefore, also gives children an opportunity to practise soldering.

### Vocabulary

LED (light-emitting diode), soldering iron, solder.

### Preparation

A sample 'Entertaining display' needs to be completed to give children an idea of what the activity involves.

### Resources needed

Pictures/clip art, cardboard, aluminium foil, brass paper fasteners, foamboard, battery holders, battery clips, batteries, wire, LEDs, a copy of photocopiable sheet 153 for each child.

### What to do

Tell the children that they are going to make a small display that will light up. The 'display' could be an advertisement or something to entertain a small child – perhaps it could illustrate a poem or story that they particularly like.

Show them step-by-step what they are going to do with an example of your own, such as a cat (as shown on photocopiable sheet 153). In particular show them how to make a push switch from a piece of card with a hinge, a piece of aluminium foil and a brass paper fastener. At this stage you should demonstrate the correct use of a soldering iron. The two pieces of wire which are to be joined should be twisted together, and then held firmly using a G-cramp or a pair of pliers. Using the soldering iron, heat up the joint, and when it is hot apply some solder, which will quickly melt. Then remove both the soldering iron and the solder. Do not move the joint until it has cooled for about 20 seconds (see diagram).

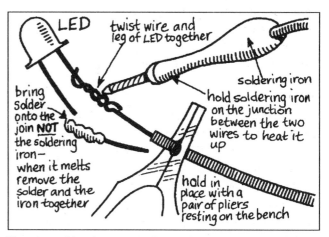

Photocopiable sheet 153 shows the important steps that the groups need to go through. Each group should choose their particular theme and then either use photographs or draw pictures to illustrate it. They should discuss with you which part of the display will light up using LEDs and which part will become the push switch.

**DESIGN AND TECHNOLOGY**

## Suggestion(s) for extension

The models could incorporate motors and buzzers as well as LEDs. The motor could make the bow-tie of a clown revolve, and a buzzer could be used as a car horn.

## Suggestion(s) for support

Children could make a model exactly as described on photocopiable sheet 153.

## Assessment opportunities

The children's knowledge of circuits and ability to solder can be assessed in this activity.

## Opportunities for IT

The children could use an art or drawing package to create the background picture for their display. They could also use clip art to help them, or scanned pictures from their own line drawings.

More able children could go on to control the circuit they have made using a computer control package with links the LEDs to a 'control box' linked to the computer. By using a simple programming language like Data Harvest's CONTACT, the children arrange to turn all of the lights on and off at set times or intervals. More adventurous sequences could be set up (although this would require different circuitry) to turn on lights in succession or groups of lights at the same time.

## Display ideas

Each model should be mounted on a display board for children to try out.

## Reference to photocopiable sheet

Sheet 153 gives detailed instructions of how this particular model is made.

## MAKING A MEMBRANE SWITCH — FPT

*To make a membrane switch, which can be used to detect a person entering or leaving the classroom.*

🕐 *Working in pairs.*

†† *Two one-hour sessions.*

⚠ *Take care when using the craft knife. Demonstrate its safe use. Make sure children are familiar with using a metal safety rule and a cutting mat.*

## Previous skills/knowledge needed

Children will need to have investigated a wide range of bought and home-made switches, and be familiar with a simple electric circuit and the concept of a switch – a break in the circuit.

## Key background information

Membrane switches are used increasingly in everyday life – the school's *Concept Keyboard*, the timer on a microwave and touch sensitive tills are some examples. It is effectively a push switch that is normally open, that is, no electricity flows unless the switch is pressed. It is relatively cheap to buy and make, and can produce a good quality switch for inclusion in many models.

The two surfaces of aluminium foil, which are the switch contacts, are kept slightly apart by a sheet of thick card with a square hole in it. When the switch is pressed, the two pieces of aluminium are forced together and contact is made. When released, the natural 'springiness' of the material causes the aluminium foil sheets to separate again.

## Vocabulary

Normally open, membrane.

## Preparation

You will need photocopiable sheet 153, which shows the construction details of the membrane switch, and the individual pieces of card, foil and wire already prepared so that you can demonstrate how the switch is made. You will need one already completed which is connected up to a battery and buzzer.

## Resources needed

Thick cardboard, aluminium foil, paper or plastic bag, multi-strand wire, PVA glue stick/clear non-solvent based adhesive, battery and battery holder, low voltage buzzer, block electrical connectors, craft knife, metal safety rule, cutting mat, wire cutters, small screwdriver, copies of photocopiable sheet 154 for each pair, extra paper.

## What to do

Remind the children of the reason for having a switch – you do not want most electrical things on all the time – and remind them of the different types of switch they have looked at.

(See 'Switches' on page 79.) Explain that you want a buzzer to sound whenever someone walks into or out of the classroom so that you can welcome a visitor or find out why someone has left the room (without permission). Discuss the possibilities and then focus in on a pressure/membrane switch which could be placed on the floor by the door.

Revise the principle of the switch – two pieces of metal touching each other – and clarify the problem you are setting. Two pieces of metal need to touch when someone walks into the room, but they should not touch once the person is right in the room. (If this was not the case, the buzzer would sound all the time and drive everyone mad!)

Show the children the basic principle of the membrane switch, and how it is made (see photocopiable sheet 154 for a diagram). Limit the size of these switches because they are intended to be prototypes, and you would be using too much material.

Use two pieces of 15cm square cardboard, with two pieces of 12cm square aluminium foil. Carefully cut an 11cm square hole in the centre of one of the pieces of cardboard using a craft knife. Show how the multi-strand wire should be bared and spread out so that there is a large area of contact and how it should be placed either side of each piece of aluminium foil so as to make a good contact. One piece of aluminium foil should be stuck to the bottom card with clear solvent-free adhesive. Do not get adhesive between the foil and the wire – the adhesive may act as an insulation – you can use a small piece of masking tape over the plastic coating to keep it firmly in place. The other piece of aluminium foil should be stuck to the top card in the same way.

Finally, cover the whole sandwich with a 15cm square of paper or a piece of thick plastic cut out of a plastic bag. The

children should put quite long leads on to the switch, so that the battery and buzzer do not need to be placed too near the door. Set up the membrane switch with a battery and buzzer using circuit blocks to make the connection.

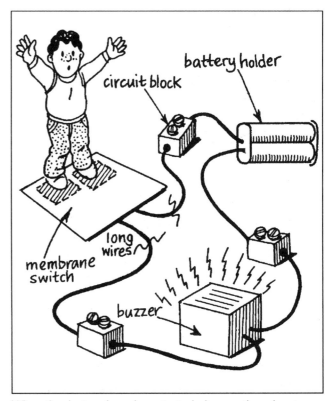

When the devices have been tested, discuss the advantages and disadvantages of the product. For example: if it is too small it might be possible to step over it and miss it; the buzzer may not be loud enough; when it is hidden under a mat, it may not work quite as well due to the lack of pressure.

DESIGN AND TECHNOLOGY

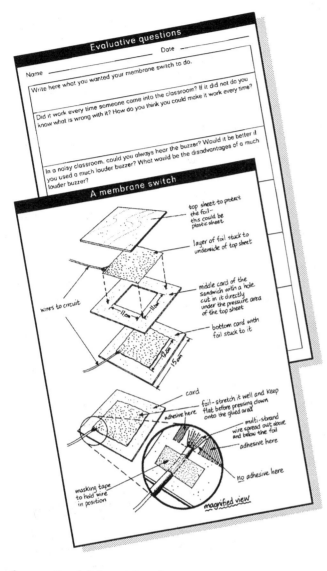

**Evaluative questions**

Date

Name

Write here what you wanted your membrane switch to do.

Did it work every time someone came into the classroom? If it did not do you know what is wrong with it? How do you think you could make it work every time?

In a noisy classroom, could you always hear the buzzer? Would it be better if you used a much louder buzzer? What would be the disadvantages of a much louder buzzer?

**A membrane switch**

top sheet to protect the foil – this could be plastic sheet

layer of foil stuck to underside of top sheet

middle card of the sandwich with a hole cut in it directly under the pressure area of the top sheet

bottom card with foil stuck to it

wires to circuit

11cm 11cm

15cm

card

foil – stretch it well and keep flat before pressing down onto the glued area

adhesive here

multi-strand wire spread out above and below the foil

adhesive here

no adhesive here

masking tape to hold wire in position

magnified view

## Display ideas

The membrane switches could be incorporated into a wall display: 'Press this to see the monster's eyes light up.' 'Press this to see the clown's bow-tie spin.' The advantage of using this type of switch in this situation, is that bulbs and motors cannot be left on accidentally.

## Reference to photocopiable sheets

Sheet 154 gives the construction of the membrane switch in diagrammatic form. Sheet 155 gives a general evaluation sheet framework which can be used where children need to be given a structure to help them evaluate their work.

# PROTECTING YOUR VALUABLES ⬦ FPT

*To make use of their knowledge of switches in a problem-solving context. To design and make a device which would protect something valuable on display.*

†† *Working in pairs.*

🕐 *Two one-hour sessions.*

⚠ *Use dry batteries. Do not use rechargeable batteries or low voltage power supplies.*

## Previous skills/knowledge needed

Ideally the children will have completed the IDEAs 'Evaluating torches' and 'Switches' on pages 78 and 79. They will also need to be aware of the use of switches in simple circuits and of buzzers and lights for warning. They should ideally be able to solder, although connections could be made in alternative ways in this activity.

## Suggestion(s) for extension

Use photocopiable sheet 155 to provide the children with a framework for a structured evaluation of the product. Some groups could make a larger version for permanent use in the classroom, or the school generally – a device could be placed at the entrance to the school.

A similar principle can be used for a multi-membrane switch, which can be used to operate a number of features of a child's model, or be incorporated into a game.

## Suggestion(s) for support

Using the parts you have already prepared, show individual groups how the 'sandwich' is made up, and particularly how the bared wire is kept firmly in place.

## Assessment opportunities

Look at the quality of the product produced. In particular focus upon the measuring, accuracy of cutting and the use of adhesives in appropriate quantities. This is a good activity for assessing the care with which children undertake a making activity, because the switches will not work well unless the instructions are followed very carefully.

**DESIGN AND TECHNOLOGY**

## Key background information

The activity 'Making a membrane switch' on page 82 has as its application the detection of people entering the classroom. It is a very focused activity concentrating mainly on the construction of a membrane switch which can be used widely in design and technology activities. It is therefore suggested that in this activity a membrane switch is not offered as one of the options. The focus here is very much on using the particular properties of a range of switches and incorporating them unobtrusively into a display. Typical solutions would involve a tremble switch, a tilt switch or a reed switch and magnet. These can be either 'home-made' or commercially available devices.

## Preparation

Have a selection of commercially available switches and home-made ones for the introduction. You will need copies of photocopiable sheets 151 and 152 available for reference.

## Resources needed

Copies of photocopiable sheets 151 and 152, a selection of different switches including a push switch, a slide switch, a toggle or rocker switch, a push-to-make switch, a push-to-break switch, a reed switch and magnet, a tilt switch and a micro switch; a range of materials such as wood, card, fabrics, adhesives, buzzers, lamps, lampholders, batteries, battery holders and battery clips.

## What to do

Set the scene that the children have to protect some valuable exhibit in a museum. They can choose what they want to protect (something they bring in from home perhaps). Tell them that at the end of the project they will have to set up their warning device and you will try to steal it without the alarm going off. You might decide that some of the best devices will be used around the school to protect trophies, pictures or perhaps computers!

Remind the children of the work they have done in science on circuits and the work they have done on switches in design and technology. Show them the buzzers and warning lights that are available and the different kinds of switch which they could use. (NB: not a membrane switch). They should also be made aware of the other materials which they can use in order to make the product.

Once the pairs have decided on the article they wish to protect, they can brainstorm some ideas of how this could be done with the resources available. Sketches should be made of the ideas and you should comment on them before they start experimenting:

▲ Have they access to all the materials they have said they will need to use?

▲ Can the device be hidden effectively?

▲ What will the finished product look like?

▲ Will it be painted, varnished or covered in fabric?

In this activity they should be encouraged to make rough prototypes first which are then developed into high quality products later. Emphasise that these would be on display in a museum and should not detract from the exhibit itself. (You wouldn't display a £500 000 necklace on a cornflake packet!)

Once the devices are finished, each pair should set theirs up with their exhibit in part of the classroom. You can then attempt to remove the 'valuable' and escape from the classroom before the alarm goes off!

## Suggestion(s) for extension

Children could research into alternative warning devices, rather than a buzzer.

## Suggestion(s) for support

Certain groups could be given a particular method to work on, rather than having to choose their own approach, for example: 'Fix a tilt switch carefully to the object so that the mercury inside is not completing the circuit. When the object is moved, what happens?'

## Assessment opportunities

For those groups who are not given a particular solution, this activity can be used to see how effectively children can select from a range of possible solutions.

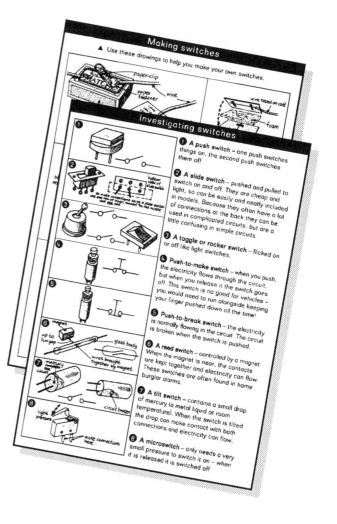

## Opportunities for IT

Older or more able children could link their security system to a computer which controls the actions of several different warning devices (for example, flashing lights, buzzers) which come on at different times or intervals. The activity could be extended further by looking at sensors other than switches (movement, heat, sound or light sensors) which could be linked to a computer and then used to set off warning devices.

## Display ideas

The most effective form of display would be for the devices to be in actual use throughout the school.

## Reference to photocopiable sheets

Sheet 151 shows the range of switches which are available and sheet 152 shows how to make some home-made switches which may be incorporated into the children's models. They will have looked at these switches in some detail if they have completed the 'Switches' activity on page 79.

## MAKING A BUGGY    ◇ FPT

*To make a simple four-wheeled buggy which is motorised. To know about the use of pulleys to slow down the rotation of a motor.*

†† *Working in pairs.*

🕐 *Three one-hour sessions.*

⚠ *Children should take care when using a saw. When using a drill, the work should be fixed firmly in place using a bench hook and/or a G-cramp.*

## Previous skills/knowledge needed

Children will need to have had experience of making simple buggies using construction kits. They will have worked with square-section wood to produce frameworks. They will also have built electric circuits using LEDs and used a soldering iron.

## Key background information

In order to make an effective motorised buggy, the wheels and axles must move freely in the axle holders, and the fast speed and low turning force in the motor must be transformed into a lower speed and higher turning force. This is done by using a small pulley wheel on the motor and linking it by a belt drive to a much larger pulley on the axle of the front or rear wheels (see Figure 4.1).

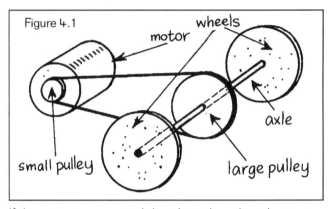

Figure 4.1

If the motor is connected directly to the axle without using differently sized pulleys it is possible that the wheels will go round quite quickly, but as soon as the buggy is placed on the floor, the friction between the wheels and the floor's surface will be greater than the force which the motor can exert – so it will just stay still (see Figure 4.2).

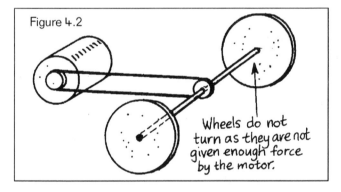

Figure 4.2

Wheels do not turn as they are not given enough force by the motor.

By using a pair of differently sized pulleys (or gear wheels if preferred), the wheel and axle turns more slowly than the motor, but with a greater force, and this can be enough to overcome friction. The direction of rotation of the motor depends on which way round the battery is connected to the connections on the motor. Another way of changing the direction would be to put a twist in the drive belt (see Figure 4.3).

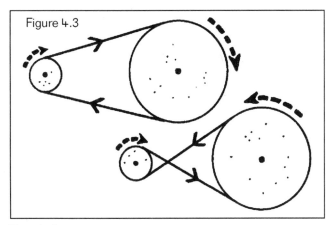

Figure 4.3

## Vocabulary
Buggy.

## Preparation
The appropriate components from a construction kit need to be removed from the box to avoid confusion when the children start experimenting with their ideas. Check that all the batteries work. Build a simple four-wheeled buggy (without a motor) for use in the introduction. Have a model wooden motorised buggy available to show to those who are having difficulties.

## Resources needed
Components from a construction kit limited to a basic framework, axles, wheels, pulleys, motor, battery holder, switch, drive belt. Square-section wood, cardboard, PVA adhesive, dowel, wooden wheels, large pulley, small pulley fixed to motor, motor holder, battery holder, battery clip, batteries, elastic band, slide switch, water-based varnish, glass paper, saw, bench hook, G-cramp, drill, drill bit, a copy of photocopiable sheet 156 for each child.

## What to do
Tell the children that they are going to experiment with a construction kit to try to make a motorised buggy. Show them the limited range of components which they are going to be able to use and ask them to find ways of making the buggy move along using a motor. Depending on the construction kit which you have available, you will have to say whether the batteries should be fixed to the buggy or whether they can be used remotely. The battery packs in some kits will be very heavy and the weight will prevent the buggy from moving. Emphasise the need to link the motor to the wheel and axle using a drive belt (elastic band) and encourage them to experiment with different sizes of pulley on both the motor and the wheel and axle.

In their pairs ask children what they are discovering:
▲ What happens when you connect the motor directly to the axle?
▲ Why do you need a drive belt at all – couldn't the motor be linked directly to the axle itself?
▲ What happens when there is a twist in the drive belt?

In a class discussion decide on the important lessons that have been learned. These should be clearly written down.
▲ With a small pulley on the motor and a large pulley on the wheel and axle, the wheels rotate more slowly than the motor, but with a greater force.
▲ With a large pulley on the motor and a small pulley on the wheel and axle, the wheels rotate very quickly, but with very little force.
▲ With equal-sized pulleys, for example an elastic band around a small pulley on the motor and then around the axle itself, the motor and wheels will go round at the same speed – again this will be too fast with too little force.

**DESIGN AND TECHNOLOGY**

▲ The wheels on the buggy usually go round when it is held in the air, but unless they are going round quite slowly and with a lot of force, the wheels do not go round when they are in contact with the floor – this is because they cannot overcome the friction. You need the wheels to go round slowly and strongly, not quickly and weakly!

▲ A twist in the drive belt can change the direction of the buggy wheels.

The children should now be in a position to make their own buggy using square-section wood, motors and pulleys. Give photocopiable sheet 156 to the children which gives a basic outline of the construction. Emphasise the importance of accuracy in measuring, cutting and drilling if they are to produce a quality product, that is one that works effectively, can stand up to sensible use, and is finished off well. Remind children of the skills which they will need to use in order to complete the model. These include accurate cutting and drilling, use of small amounts of PVA adhesive, wiring up a simple circuit, and soldering. Using photocopiable sheet 156 as an outline, the children should be asked to put together a list of the tasks and the order in which they need to be done. They should also indicate which of the pair will be responsible for each task.

The groups should then start making their models. On completion of their model each pair should produce an evaluation of it and their plan:

▲ Did things go to plan?

▲ Did they have to change the order?

▲ Were the jobs shared out equally?

▲ Were there any disagreements?

▲ Did the model work well?

▲ How could it be improved?

### Suggestion(s) for extension

Once the models are complete they could design a cardboard net to cover the buggy and transform it into a type of vehicle. Particular care should be taken in ensuring that the switch is still accessible through the net. Children could also incorporate other electrical features into their models such as headlamps.

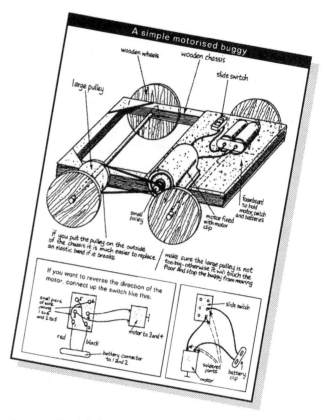

### Suggestion(s) for support

Each pair could be given a completed construction kit model which worked. This could be used in conjunction with photocopiable sheet 156 to give a clear structure to the activity. The children could also be given a list of the jobs that must be done and these tasks could be allocated to particular individuals.

### Assessment opportunities

This activity gives you a good opportunity to assess the children's understanding of pulley systems. Questioning them during the problem-solving process can be a particularly effective form of assessment.

### Opportunities for IT

The children could use a drawing or simple CAD package to draft the design for their buggy. These could be printed out with a word-processed evaluation of the final model for use in a classroom display. Alternatively, the drawings and evaluations could be combined using a word processor or desktop publishing package and each group's work combined to make a class book of designs.

### Display ideas

The planning sheet, evaluation sheet and model of each pair should be displayed together. This will give an opportunity to focus upon the importance of both planning and evaluation.

### Reference to photocopiable sheet

Sheet 156 shows the outline of a basic buggy structure.

# Control

This section inevitably extends the work the children will have done on electricity and to that extent it can often be used to extend existing activities rather than offering activities in their own right.

It is important to realise that control does not necessarily mean computers and that a useful teaching strategy is to devise a system that needs a number of hand-operated switches, and when the children realise that it becomes very tedious to switch switches on and off repeatedly in a particular pattern, suggest that a machine that could be used to undertake such repetitive tasks might be a computer.

Consideration should also be given to the considerable level of resourcing that computer control requires, and that it is currently not feasible, in most schools, for it to be done as a whole class activity. The implications of this are that activities involving computer control should be viewed as extension activities for some children in the class, usually at the later stages of Key Stage 2.

# FLASHING LIGHTS   ◆ FPT

*To develop an existing product of their own.*
*To explore some form of automatic control.*

**††** *Making individually/discussion as a group.*
**🕐** *Two one-hour sessions.*
**⚠** *Use dry batteries as the source of the electricity.*

## Previous skills/knowledge needed

This activity allows for an addition to be made to an existing project. Children need to have made a motorised vehicle. They should also have looked at a wide range of different switches and understand the fundamentals of basic electrical circuits.

## Key background information

A reed switch allows electricity to flow when a magnet is placed nearby. If a reed switch is fixed to the chassis and a small magnet is fixed inside the wheel, as the wheel rotates the magnet gets nearer and farther away from the reed switch, causing a light to switch on and off. This activity allows children to fix a flashing light to their vehicle to make it into a police car, ambulance or fire-engine (see Figure 8.1).

## Vocabulary

Reed switch.

## Preparation

Have a model prepared which includes a reed switch and a magnet causing a light to switch on and off. This could be a vehicle or a lighthouse for example. Ensure all the children have a vehicle made in another activity (see page 86).

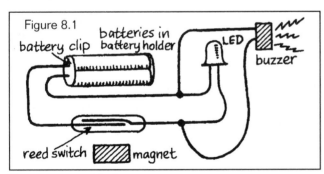

Figure 8.1

## Resources needed

Reed switches, magnets, wire, LEDs or lamps, solder, soldering irons, clear non-solvent based adhesive, models from previous session, previously prepared 'reed switch' model.

## What to do

Look at the vehicles the children have completed. Talk about how some vehicles make themselves noticed in the traffic so that other road users get out of the way (flashing lights, sirens on police cars, ambulances and fire-engines.)

Ask the children for ideas on how a flashing light could be controlled automatically. In particular, remind them of the work they have done on different kinds of switches. Direct them towards a magnet and a reed switch and ask them how they think it might work. If necessary, show them your model. They should draw annotated sketches to show how to incorporate the device into their model. Now they add the reed switch, magnet and LED to their existing model, using the same batteries, battery clips and battery holders that are used to power the motor.

## Suggestion(s) for extension

The children could incorporate a buzzer into the circuit to provide an intermittent horn (buzzing) sound (see Figure 8.1).

## Suggestion(s) for support

The children should be given your prepared model so that they can see how the reed switch and the rest of the circuit is arranged.

## Assessment opportunities

This activity provides opportunities to see how effectively the children can develop a solution with varying degrees of assistance. The annotated sketches will also identify the degree to which the children understand simple electric circuits.

## Opportunities for IT

The children could extend this activity by replacing the reed switch with a computer to control the flashing light or buzzer. In this case they will need a control box which enables the electrical circuits to be connected to the computer. The children will then need to be taught how to set up the circuit using the control box and how to use the control software to write a series of instructions which automatically operate the lights on the model. Earlier forms of control language used commands similar to LOGO, with instructions to turn on the different outputs (lights or buzzers), wait for a given period of time and then turn them off. More recent software uses pictures to help children identify different outputs and program them.

## Display ideas

The models should be put on display, together with the sketches of how the flashing light circuit works.

# REVERSING BUGGIES   ◆ FPT

*To learn how to use a two-way switch to reverse a motor.*
**††** *Working in pairs and then individually.*
**🕐** *Three two-hour sessions.*
**⚠** *Take care when using a saw. Hold wood firmly on a bench hook fixed with a G-cramp.*

## Previous skills/knowledge needed

This is a very advanced project which should be attempted only by children who have competently produced a wide range of models incorporating electrical devices.

DESIGN AND
TECHNOLOGY

## Key background information

There are two factors which need to be understood in order to get this model to work. Firstly, one piece of wood protrudes from the front and the rear of the buggy. When the buggy hits a wall, the piece of wood is made to slide and this causes the contacts to change, reversing the motor. When the buggy hits another obstruction the piece of wood slides back to its original position, once again causing the vehicle to go forward.

The second factor is the actual electrical circuit which is shown below.

When the wood is protruding from the left of the buggy, the drawing pins and brass paper fasteners are making contact, and the motor is travelling in one direction (see Figure 8.2). On hitting a wall the wood protrudes from the right of the vehicle, the contacts change position, and the motor is now moved in the opposite direction. These two ideas need to be incorporated into the initial simple buggy (see Figure 8.3).

This is a prototyping exercise so the children need only scraps of material, wood and drawing pins.

## Vocabulary

Control, two-way switch.

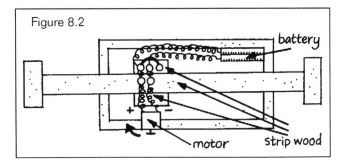

Figure 8.2

## Preparation

The children should have made an ordinary buggy which they are then able to develop into an automatically reversing one. It would probably be useful to make a reversing buggy yourself to make sure you are familiar with some of the practical problems that can be encountered during construction.

## Resources needed

Original buggies (see page 86), square-section wood, brass paper fasteners, drawing pins, wire, solder, soldering irons, motors, batteries, battery holders, battery clips, two-way sliding switches, saws, PVA adhesive, bench hooks, G-cramps, paper and pencils.

## What to do

This activity should only be introduced to the children who have completed a simple four-wheeled motorised buggy. Ask the children to demonstrate their models. What are the problems with them? The most obvious one is what happens when it hits a wall or other obstacle. How could you design a system so that the vehicle automatically reversed and carried on moving in the opposite direction?

Give each pair a motor, a battery, a battery holder and a battery clip and ask them to find out how the motor can be made to rotate one way, and then the other. The basic principle they need to discover is that it depends on the battery connections (see diagrams below). Figure 8.3 shows the system using wood and drawing pins, and Figure 8.4 is a system using a sliding two-way switch.

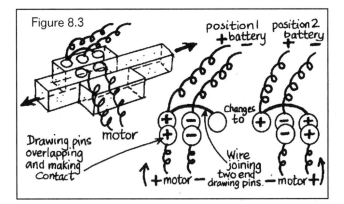

Figure 8.3

Once the children are familiar with the principle, see if they can come up with a system to automatically change the battery connections over (without disconnecting them!). They can then design a way of using this device so that it will automatically reverse the motor when the buggy hits a wall.

The children should be supported with their own ideas and by careful questioning led to a solution. They should first sketch their ideas and show how they will be incorporated into their existing buggy. Once they are happy with their solutions, they can incorporate them into their buggies.

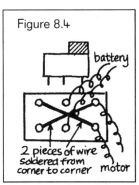

Figure 8.4

## Suggestion(s) for extension

A net can be produced which can be attached to the buggy to make it look like a particular type of vehicle.

## Suggestion(s) for support

This activity should be attempted only by children who have shown themselves to be competent in construction techniques and electrical work. Nevertheless, there may be times when they need support on a one-to-one basis to get over particular problems. One of the most common difficulties is achieving good electrical contact between sets of drawing pins – rub them with a file to make sure the contact surfaces are clean.

## Assessment opportunities

A child who manages to build this vehicle satisfactorily with little support will be demonstrating a high level of practical skill and a clear problem-solving strategy. You will be able to make judgements about the children who need more of your support.

## Opportunities for IT

For more able children this activity could be extended to use a sensor to detect when the buggy is close to the wall. This sensor would then be used to control the direction of the motor so that the buggy would be reversed away from the wall.

## Display ideas

The finished models will make a very impressive display. It could also include the sketches which the children made as they were solving the initial problem.

# TRAFFIC LIGHTS  FPT

*To develop children's knowledge about switches and control. To develop the ability to write a control program to automate the switching sequence.*

†† *Working in groups of four.*

🕐 *Three two-hour sessions.*

⚠ *Ensure that the interface box is already connected to the computer and to the mains electrical supply, if appropriate. Make sure the children are supervised when using the soldering irons.*

## Previous skills/knowledge needed

Children will need to have worked with a wide range of simple switches. They should have used LEDs and be familiar with safe soldering techniques.

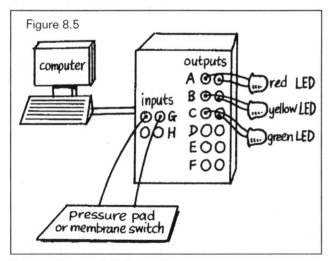

Figure 8.5

## Key background information

This activity gives children an opportunity to control simple traffic lights using manual switches, but shows children that as the system gets more complex, an automatic system is to be preferred. The activity does not assume any particular computer control software or hardware. (The information which follows is appropriate to all control activities.)

In a computer control activity the computer basically acts as a timer which can turn switches on and off. An interface box needs to be connected to the computer, and the bulbs and motors are connected to its outputs. The computer can

then be used to switch these devices on and off. The interface can also have some inputs which can send messages to the computer. The simple example illustrated in Figure 8.6 shows how a typical computer control system will work.

This interface box has six outputs and two inputs. The LEDs of the traffic lights are connected to outputs A, B and C. The pressure mat which detects if a car approaches the traffic lights is connected to input G. A program of a form similar to the one below needs to be written.

> Switch A on (Red traffic light stays on)
> If pressure pad G is pressed
> **Switch A off, Switch B on for 2 seconds**
> (Red light goes off/amber light goes on)
> **Switch B off, Switch C on for 10 seconds**
> (Amber light goes off/green light goes on)
> **Switch C off, Switch B on for 2 seconds**
> (Green light goes off/ amber light goes on)
> **Switch B off, Switch A on**
> (Amber light goes off/red light goes on)
> **Go back to the start of the program**
> (Red light stays on until pressure pad G is pressed again)

This is obviously a very simplified system – normally there would be another set of traffic lights at the junction which would have a different sequence, and these could be connected to outputs D, E and F. Each computer interface box and associated software has its own particular instructions and these should be taught to the children at the beginning of the activity.

## Vocabulary

Interface, input, output.

## Preparation

Have red, yellow and green LEDs wired up to a simple three-way switch made up of drawing pins and paper-clips. Set up a computer with an interface box and a pressure pad as a detection device. For the extension activity, paint a small crossroads junction layout onto a base board. Make sure you know how the computer program works. Due to the complexity of this activity, you may wish to work with one group of four at a time, while the rest of the class work on something else.

## Resources needed

Red, yellow and green LEDs, square-section wood, wire, solder, soldering irons, materials for making switches, drawing pins, computers, control software, interface boxes, corrugated cardboard, paints, paintbrushes.

## What to do

Remind the children of the work they have done on switches and LEDs. Show them your model traffic lights (three LEDs fixed together in a wooden stand, with three pairs of wires) and the bits and pieces which can be used to make a two- or three-way switch. With the children's help, set up a circuit

DESIGN AND TECHNOLOGY

that will make the LEDs give the traffic light sequence of red, red/amber, green, amber, red. A possible circuit is shown below (Figure 8.6).

Through discussion, it should become obvious that this procedure would be best computerised. Connect the three LEDs to three outputs of the interface box. Show the children how to use the computer program to set up the correct sequence of lights. Set the children their task, which is to program two sets of traffic lights as they would work on a road junction. They should now make the two sets of traffic lights, and set them out on a base board. Their solution should look something like Figure 8.7.

### Suggestion(s) for extension
A second set of traffic lights (connected in parallel with the first set) could be set up on the other corners of the road junction. Use the pedestrian crossing prepared earlier on one of the junctions. This could then include a red figure, a green figure, a flashing green figure, a buzzing noise and a push button to set the sequence in operation.

### Suggestion(s) for support
Some groups may need to be reminded of the sequence of two sets of traffic lights, that is, one is on red when the other is on green. They might also need to be reminded that the leads from the second set of traffic lights should go to outputs D, E and F.

### Assessment opportunities
This activity will assess how well the children can set up a logical control program.

### Display ideas
The complete road junction displays, together with their traffic lights and some model cars can be put on display. A different model could be connected to a computer each day of the week.

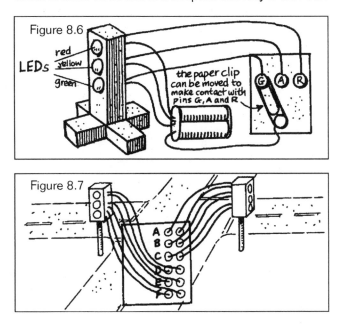

Figure 8.6

LEDs  red  yellow  green

the paper clip can be moved to make contact with pins G, A and R

G  A  R

Figure 8.7

A
B
C
D
E
F

---

### INTERACTIVE MUSEUM DISPLAYS   FPT

*To develop knowledge of control using a membrane keypad followed by a computer.*
†† *Working in groups of four.*
🕐 *Four two-hour sessions.*
⚠ *Make sure you use only dry batteries as the source of electricity. An adult should plug the computer interface box into the mains and the computer. Make sure that the appropriate safety cutting tools are used.*

### Previous skills/knowledge needed
Children should have had considerable experience of working with electrical and mechanical components and a range of construction materials, particularly in sheet form. They need to be able to solder and should have made a simple membrane switch. They should also be able to use a computer control package if you want them to undertake the extension work.

### Key background information
This activity gives children an opportunity to develop their skills using electrical and mechanical components in order to create the sort of interactive display that you would find in many modern museums – for example, by pressing buttons, lights light up and part of the display may rotate to show other features of the exhibit. Begin this activity using a membrane keypad, but it would be possible to connect some of the electrical components to the outputs of a computer which could then be programmed to go through particular sequences. This activity can be designed to fit in with any topic the children are doing which requires the presentation of their findings.

### Vocabulary
Membrane, keypad, computer interface.

### Preparation
You need to build a typical display to show the children the sort of thing that is required. For example, if they were doing a project on animals, the display could be on tigers. One switch would light up a photograph (ideally, a transparency) of a tiger. If this is mounted into the display, with a light behind it, then the picture could only be seen well when the light is actually on. Then there could be a clip art map of the world, with a coloured LED marking the places where tigers can be found, which light up when a second switch is pressed. There could perhaps be a question about tigers, with four alternative answers, and the correct one lights up when you press the third button, and finally you might have a fourth switch connected to a motorised geared-down turntable which brings plastic models of male, female and young tigers

**DESIGN AND TECHNOLOGY**

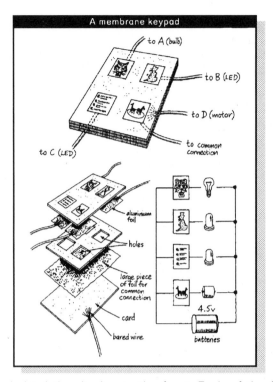

from behind the display to the front. Each of the four membrane switches should have appropriate labels such as 'Which animal am I?', 'Where do I live?', 'What are my young called?' and 'Here is my family.'

Alternatively, you could have the display connected to four outputs of a computer interface box so that the parts of the display are timed and lit up in sequence. The sequence could be made to start when an appropriate input was received by the computer such as a button being pushed, or someone standing on a pressure pad near the display. (See Figure 8.8.)

### Resources needed
Square-section wood, cardboard, aluminium foil, glue stick, PVA adhesive, masking tape, foamboard, thick cardboard, corrugated plastic, gears, pulleys, elastic bands, clear acetate film, craft knives, metal safety rules, cutting mats, soldering irons, solder, electrical connection blocks, batteries, battery holders, battery clips, LEDs, motors, motor clips, wire, computers, clip art packages, drawing packages, control packages, a copy of photocopiable sheet 157 for each child.

### What to do
Start the session by demonstrating your museum-type display to the class. Explain that it is made up of switches and other electrical components with which they are familiar. Talk about a topic that they are covering at the moment. In groups of four they should think about what they could display and what information they could give to other people. They then need to think of interactive ways of providing this information. Ask them to sketch their ideas and show you before commencing their display. Give out photocopiable page 157 and explain that, initially, you want them to use a membrane keypad and then they can move on to computers.

### Suggestion(s) for extension
The display could be controlled by a computer rather than simple switches. A simple push switch could start the sequence off, or a pressure-sensitive mat (see 'Protecting your valuables' on page 84) could be used so that the display starts operating when someone comes near.

### Suggestion(s) for support
Some children will require support in thinking of the information which they would like to display. They could use ordinary push-to-make switches rather than making a membrane keypad. Some groups may need to copy your example rather than come up with a display of their own.

### Assessment opportunities
Children who make a display successfully will show considerable skills in planning, designing and their understanding of control.

### Opportunities for IT
This activity could be extended to a computer-controlled display. A pressure pad could be used to detect when someone approaches the display. This would be linked to the computer which would then run through a series of short control loops, perhaps to turn on the light, make parts of the display move or control a tape recorder which gives information about the display.

### Display ideas
The displays could be set up in the main entrance hall of the school for visitors to try out.

### Reference to photocopiable sheet
Photocopiable page 157 shows the basic construction of a membrane keypad which can be used to switch a number of different devices on and off.

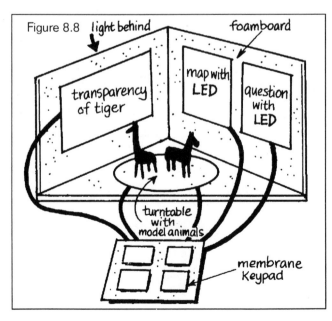

# Design and make assignments

These assignments must give children opportunities to show that they can operate at particular National Curriculum levels in designing and making. All of the skills of designing and making will have been practised in the focused activities that the children will have undertaken, but these design and make assignments, above all, give children an opportunity to select the materials and the techniques that they are going to use themselves, and let them identify their own needs, albeit in contexts provided by the teacher.

However, there still has to be a structure for the activity, and in order to make it manageable in the classroom it has to be undertaken under specific constraints, for example, you will not be able to have an unlimited supply of materials in the classroom. Children should be aware of these constraints, after all, in the 'real world' designers have to work within the limitations given to them by their clients. In all these activities, it would be possible to change the constraints so that the activities fit in with the materials and facilities which you have available.

**DESIGN AND TECHNOLOGY**

# THE NATURE OF DESIGN AND MAKE ASSIGNMENTS

When discussing work with children it is vital that you offer at least two or three alternative approaches to each aspect of the task. If you offer only one method, then children will be unable to show that they are able to make choices about how to go about this particular task, and are therefore unable to show that they can operate at higher levels of design and technology capability.

On the other hand it is also important to remember that a design and make assignment is not an examination where you are not allowed to help or teach the children anything. When you look back on the activity in order to match the child to a level statement you will be making an overall generalised judgement about what that child knows and can do, rather than one related to the number of mistakes the child made or the number of times help was asked for.

A design and make assignment gives children greater freedom than IDEAs and FPTs, and you need to be able to encourage children to work on more difficult, and hopefully more stimulating projects. But do not encourage them to undertake too complex an activity which you end up making yourself! Discussing the children's work with them during the planning stages enables you to prevent this.

As a Design and Make Assignment is the vehicle for assessing the Level at which children are operating in their design and technology work, the format of the following activities is a little different. In particular, the following two sections are applicable to any design and make assignment.

### Suggestion(s) for support

If a child needs continual support from an adult or a peer in the group then there is no reason why it should not be given, although the temptation to actually do the project for them must be avoided. You will clearly be aware of the Level of support that the child is needing and this will be reflected in the Level which you finally award them. Remember that the Levels are awarded for their capability to engage in the designing and making process, not solely for the standard of the finished product.

### Assessment opportunities

These activities give you the opportunity to assess both the children's designing skills (their ability to think up ideas, to do research, to sketch their ideas, to plan their work, to try things out and to evaluate their designs) and their making skills (their ability to work accurately with a range of materials and tools, to plan their project and to evaluate their prototypes and finished products). When the children have completed an activity you can use the verbal, written and practical evidence you will have collected to decide which of the Level Descriptions for Attainment Target 1: *Designing*

and Attainment Target 2: *Making* best describe the work of that child. Remember that this is a 'best fit' approach. All you need is the evidence to support your assertion, although it should not be necessary to retain all the evidence of all the children in the class. More appropriately, the school should compile a portfolio of children's work which contains photographs, drawings and evaluation sheets of typical work at each level. It should include work from different classes and different academic years, and should be reviewed as some new work is added and other pieces taken away. This work will provide an essential moderation instrument within the school and will provide new members of staff with a vital measure as to the appropriate quality of work at each level.

### Opportunities for IT

In this chapter the IT section has been altered to provide teachers with a number of possible activities, linked to the design and make activity, that would enable assessment of some aspects of IT capability to be made.

Clearly, it would be impossible for a child to undertake every activity suggested, but over a period of time the teacher might wish to select a single activity that would give the child an opportunity to show her/his level of IT capability against the level descriptions in one aspect of information technology.

The teacher could suggest activities, or direct the child to a particular one, for example, over the year the child might write, edit and print out one evaluation of a DMA, or use a drawing program within the design process.

# PHOTOGRAPH FRAMES

*To design and make a photograph frame.*

†† *Working in pairs, then individually.*

🕐 *Three two-hour sessions.*

⚠ *Take care when using saws or drills. Use a cutting mat and metal safety rule when using a craft knife. Use oven gloves when putting things into, or taking them out of, the oven.*

### Possible previous skills/knowledge needed

Children will probably have worked with strip wood, PVA adhesive and cardboard corners. They may have looked at fastenings and worked with mouldable materials and decorating fabrics. They should be aware of a range of adhesives and be familiar with an appropriate range of tools and techniques for working with wood, plastic, card, fabric and mouldable materials.

### Key background information

This assignment gives children an opportunity to make a relatively simple gift for their parents, and at the same time allows them to choose from a wide range of materials. The wider the choice you can give them the better, provided that

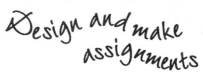

the children have been taught the skills and techniques they need to work with the materials.

## Preparation

Ask the children to look out for photograph frames in shops about two to three weeks before the activity starts. Tell them to make a list of the types that they see. Collect catalogues that contain photograph frames which can be used as reference material. About a week before the project ask the children to bring in a photograph which they would like to frame, and see if any children could borrow a photograph frame from home for the introductory lesson.

## Typical resources needed

Wood, PVA adhesive, Copydex, clear solvent-free adhesive, masking tape, cardboard, craft knives, metal safety rules, cutting mats, saws, drills, scissors, selection of fabric, corrugated plastic sheet, foamboard, Formello, knives, forks, oven gloves, protective clothing, clear acetate sheet, newspaper, paint, varnish, wallpaper paste, clay, glaze, access to an oven and kiln, paper and pencils.

## What to do

Tell the children that they are going to make a photograph frame for their parents or grandparents. (Alternatively, they could make the frames for sale at a school event.) Explain that the photograph determines the size of the photograph frame. Ask the children to look at the frames they have brought in from home. In pairs they should discuss their features, then look in catalogues and talk about the commercial frames they saw in shops in order to increase their range of ideas. Ask them to share the findings as a whole class.

Get the children to consider the wide range of materials that are used. All the time, remind them of techniques they have covered which might be appropriate. Here are some suggestions for the frame. It could:
▲ be made out of wood, then painted, varnished or covered with fabric;
▲ have Formello patterns or figures stuck to it;
▲ be covered with papier mâché to give it a different texture and shape;
▲ be rectangular or curved;
▲ be made out of clay and glazed;
▲ be made out of cardboard.

Ask the children to come up with a number of designs on paper. In particular you should question them about why they have chosen each feature:
▲ Why is it that colour?
▲ Does it match a room at home?
▲ Is it your Mum's favourite colour?
▲ Why is it that shape?
▲ Does the shape influence the material you will use?
▲ Why has the frame got painted flowers on it?
▲ Do you like flowers or are your parents keen gardeners?

Clearly there are no right or wrong answers to these questions, but by asking them you will emphasise how important it is that children understand the decisions they are making.

When the children have come up with some reasonable and practical ideas, ask them to produce a plan of action and a list of materials and equipment that they will need. Wherever possible the children should be responsible for the time planning of the project and the order in which things are done. Allocating time to an activity such as this is difficult, but there needs to be a compromise between allocating too short a period of time, where nobody achieves satisfaction in completing their product, and too long a period when the children see no urgency in completing their work and just let the activity drag on.

If you consider their planning is sufficient then they should be allowed to start making their photograph frame. Emphasise the importance of quality and continually remind them of the need for accuracy and care during construction.

## Suggestion(s) for extension

Some children could be set the task to make a frame that will hold a whole series of photographs. This will probably mean making a large background base with a cardboard mask placed over it, with different shapes cut out for each photograph. Alternatively, it could be two or three frames hinged together in some way.

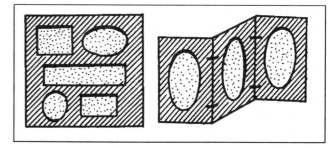

## Opportunities for IT

The children might display their IT capability by using:
▲ a drawing or CAD package to design their frame;
▲ an art or drawing package to design a border for the mount inside the frame;
▲ an art package to design and then print wrapping paper for the frame;
▲ a word processor to write instructions on how to make a similar frame;
▲ a word processor to write, edit and print an evaluation of their frame for display in the class.

## Display ideas

The photograph frames could be collected together on a wall and nearby table, each with the children's chosen photograph inside. They could be used to illustrate the wide range of materials the children are capable of working with.

**DESIGN AND TECHNOLOGY**

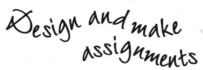
# ELECTRICAL GAMES

*To design and make an electrical game for a particular market. To choose appropriate electrical components and construction materials.*

†† *Working in groups of four.*

🕐 *Four two-hour sessions.*

⚠ *Make sure the only source of electricity available is dry batteries (not rechargeable ones which can get very hot if short-circuited). Take care when using saws and drills. Make sure children are under close supervision when using soldering irons. Use a cutting mat and metal safety rule when using a craft knife.*

### Possible previous skills/knowledge needed

Children will need to be familiar with a range of construction materials and techniques and should have undertaken focused tasks involving series and parallel circuits, switches, buzzers, LEDs, bulbs and motors. They need to have undertaken focused tasks which covered the main aspects of designing and making. Children should also be familiar with working as a member of a group.

### Key background information

There are a number of simple electrical games which are often used in science to illustrate particular circuit ideas. Quiz boards and steady-hand games are typical. The focus here, however, must be on the production of a quality product which works and which will withstand typical treatment. For example, if it is a travel game, it should be sturdy enough to withstand being carried around in a bag.

### Preparation

You need to have a number of simple electrical games available as examples. Ask your class if they have any which they could bring in. You also need to find books and catalogues which include games so that the children can use them for research.

### Typical resources needed

LEDs, bulbs, bulb holders, wire, solder, soldering irons, paper-clips, drawing pins, batteries, battery holders, battery clips, motors, buzzers, selection of switches, small pieces of sheet metal, aluminium foil, cardboard, wood, foamboard, corrugated plastic, PVA adhesive, clear acetate sheet, scissors, wire cutters, saws, craft knives, metal safety rules, cutting mats, coat-hanger wire, pulleys, elastic bands, wooden wheels, dowel, pencils and paper.

### What to do

Show the children the sample electrical games you have got. As a class discuss the main features of the games. What themes have they got? Could they be made more exciting? Who plays with them? Explain that they will be making an electrical game and they have to decide who it will be for. Is it to keep people amused on a long journey? Is it for an adult or a much younger child? In their groups they should think about this and also what the game would be like. After they have discussed some ideas, they can share them with the whole class. At this stage remind them of the skills and techniques that they could use – in particular, soldering and general circuit design.

Back in their groups, get the children to sketch their ideas and then produce a group drawing of their idea showing the materials and techniques they intend to use. Discuss these ideas thoroughly with each group. Be positive, but also challenging. Ask why they chose particular materials and why they did not include others. There are few right and wrong answers, but the way in which the group answers the questions can tell you much about the quality of their thinking. When you consider the children have come up with some reasonable and practical ideas ask them to produce a plan of action and a list of materials and equipment that they will need. They can then start making their electrical games. Emphasise the importance of quality and continually remind them of the need for accuracy and care during construction.

When the games are completed each group should evaluate their own product, and then the games should be rotated round the class so that the children see all the games and can make comments. In a final class discussion encourage constructive criticism and praise. Do not make it into a competition.

### Suggestion(s) for extension

It may be possible for some groups to make a much larger game suitable for a stall at a summer fair or other fund-raising event. This would involve additional criteria to consider, most notably, how to make it so appealing that people will want to spend their money on it!

**DESIGN AND TECHNOLOGY**

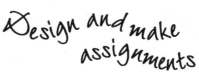
## Opportunities for IT

The children might display their IT capability by using:

▲ a drawing or CAD package to design their game;

▲ an art or drawing package to create background pictures for their games;

▲ a word processor to write instructions on how to make a similar game;

▲ a word processor to write, edit and print an evaluation of their game for display in the class;

▲ computer control to make the game more interesting and interactive.

## Display ideas

The games could be put on display to be looked at, but it would probably be better if they were actually used. Perhaps the class could make them available to children in other classes to play with at lunch-time or during a wet playtime. They could even hire them out!

## PROTOTYPE LAMPS

*To identify a market for a lamp. To design and make a prototype lamp.*

†† *Working in pairs.*

⏲ *Four two-hour sessions.*

⚠ *Only use dry batteries as the source of electricity. Do not use rechargeable ones as they get very hot if they are short-circuited. Under no circumstance should mains electricity be used in these prototypes.*

## Possible previous skills/knowledge needed

Children will need to have done work on electrical circuits, and have used a soldering iron. They should have had experience of working with wood, plastic sheet and fabric. They will also have undertaken focused tasks covering the main aspects of designing and making.

## Key background information

This activity gives children an opportunity to design a product of their own choosing for a prospective customer. By making it a prototype, the quantity of physical resources required can be kept to a minimum, as full-sized products are not required. Leave a discussion on the size of the model until you look at their final proposals. The children will definitely make use of their knowledge of electrical circuits and switches, but will also be able to call upon a large range of making skills and techniques which they will have developed through focused activities.

## Preparation

Find books and catalogues which contain pictures of a wide range of different sorts of lamps. Arrange for a local electrical shop manager to judge the finished products. It might be possible to involve an electrical firm in a project of this kind, perhaps even by their sponsoring the activity.

## Typical resources needed

Bulbs, bulb holders, plastic-coated wire, wire, batteries, battery holders, battery connectors, range of switches, materials for making the lamp such as wood strip, dowel, plastic, textiles, thin stiff wire, soldering irons, paper-clips, drawing pins, small pieces of sheet metal, aluminium foil, cardboard, wood, foamboard, corrugated plastic, PVA adhesive, clear acetate sheet, scissors, wire cutters, saws, bench hooks, G-cramps, craft knives, metal safety rules, cutting mats, coat-hanger wire, paper and pencils.

## What to do

Ask the children, in pairs, to write down as many different uses for electric lamps as they can think of. Discuss these with the whole class, writing up all the suggestions as they are offered. Tell the children that each pair is going to make a prototype electric lamp. Remind them of the term 'prototype'. It means that it does not need to be the same size or work in quite the same way as the real lamp would, but that it is still produced to a very high quality and gives people a good idea of what the lamp would actually look like. Explain that a visitor from a local electrical shop will come and judge all the lamps and decide which one he or she thinks he or she would be able to sell most of in her or his shop. At this stage remind them of the skills and techniques that they may wish to use – in particular soldering and general construction techniques. Show them the resources that are available for them to use.

Now get the children to sketch their ideas. They should make use of catalogues and books which contain pictures of lamps to help them with their designing. They should then produce a drawing of their idea showing materials and techniques they intend to use. Discuss these ideas thoroughly with each pair. They should have decided on the sort of lamp it is going to be (reading lamp, lounge lamp,

**DESIGN AND TECHNOLOGY**

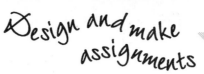
portable lamp) and the age of the potential customer (child, teenager, adult, elderly person) and have pointed out what features will make it appeal to their target group.

Ask them to produce a plan of action and a list of materials and equipment that they will need. They should then be able to start making their prototype lamps. Emphasise the importance of quality and continually remind them of the need for accuracy and care during construction. On completing their products, an exhibition can be arranged and the visitor invited to make her or his comments. Each pair should also be asked to evaluate their own work.

### Suggestion(s) for extension
Particularly able groups may be able to take the idea beyond its prototype stage to a full-sized working model, although the light source must still be battery powered. *Under no circumstances should a mains power supply be used.*

### Opportunities for IT
The children might display their IT capability by using:
▲ a drawing or CAD package to create a working design for their lamp;
▲ an art or desktop publishing package to create a poster to advertise their lamp;
▲ a word processor to write, edit and print an evaluation of their lamp for display alongside it.

### Display ideas
Each lamp should be displayed together with the original sketches and annotations, the time plan, and an evaluation of the finished product from the pair who constructed it and from the visitor from the electrical shop. The visitor could be asked to make display space available in her or his shop for the children's work.

## SLIPPERS

*To design, make and evaluate a pair of slippers for a younger child.*

†† *Working in pairs.*

🕐 *Four one-hour sessions.*

⚠ *Remind the children how important it is to take care when using pins and needles.*

### Possible previous skills/knowledge needed
Children will need to be familiar with a range of fabrics and their different properties. They should also be familiar with materials which might be appropriate for the soles of their slippers, for example, Plastazote, thick cardboard. They need to have used a wide range of adhesives and fixings which can be used to join fabric and other materials. They will also have undertaken focused tasks which will have covered the main aspects of designing and making.

### Key background information
This activity enables children to produce their own designs for a pair of slippers. They are able to choose who they are making the slippers for, the materials out of which they are going to make them, and the nature of the design. In some situations you may like to extend the materials available to include those which they bring in themselves from home.

### Preparation
Ask children to bring in a pair of slippers from home for the introductory session. If possible, have a few pairs of old slippers which the children can disassemble in order to discover how they are put together, the shapes of the individual parts and what materials they are made from. You also need to label the resources that you are prepared to make available for this activity.

### Typical resources needed
Range of fabrics, materials for soles such as Plastazote or thick cardboard, Copydex, needles, thread, pins, paper for patterns, stuffing, string, safety eyes and noses, catalogues and books showing slippers, information sheets on working with textiles.

### What to do
As a whole class, look at the slippers that people have brought in. See if it is possible to categorise them – male and female, sensible and novelty and so on. In pairs the children should be encouraged to look closely at the slippers they have brought in. What materials are they made out of? Can they see how the pieces are joined together? Then swap the slippers

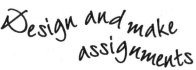
around the classroom until each group has analysed seven or eight pairs. If you have enough old slippers that can be disassembled let each pair do that now. Alternatively, the disassembly might need to be a demonstration.

The class should now have a reasonable idea of the range of slippers that are available. Show them the fabrics and other materials that they will have, and remind them of some of the other textile activities they have done and the skills they have developed. Then each pair should decide upon a young child for whom they are going to make the slippers and start designing them, making use of the books and catalogues for inspiration. They should produce a drawing of their idea showing the materials and techniques they intend to use. Discuss these ideas thoroughly with each pair. Ask why they chose particular materials and particular techniques. There are few right and wrong answers, but the way in which a pair answers them can tell you much about the quality of their thinking.

When you consider the children have come up with some reasonable and practical ideas ask them to produce a plan of action and a list of materials and equipment that they will need. They should then start making their slippers. Emphasise the importance of quality and continually remind them of the need for accuracy and care during making. When the slippers are complete the pair should give them to the child for whom they were made and ask him or her what he or she thinks. They should also make their own evaluation of the slippers.

### Suggestion(s) for extension

The children could design and make a novelty box or bag suitable for holding the slippers. They should be encouraged to make the box appealing to the young child, otherwise they might just as well use an old shoebox, rather than make one!

### Opportunities for IT

The children might display their IT capability by using:
▲ a drawing or CAD package to create a working pattern for the slippers;
▲ a drawing package to design a net for a shoebox for the slippers which they can then print and cut out;
▲ an art package to design and print wrapping paper for the slippers or their shoeboxes;
▲ a word processor to write, edit and print an evaluation of their slippers.

### Display ideas

A display incorporating the finished products, the initial designs and plans and an evaluation from the 'customer' and the 'manufacturers' will provide a great deal of useful evidence to inform your decision as to the level of capability at which you feel the children are working. A photograph of each individual display will give you a permanent record of that evidence.

# SNACKS

*To identify a market for a new snack. To design and make a snack.*

†† *Working in groups of four.*
🕐 *Four one-hour sessions.*
⚠ *All the equipment used in this activity should only be used for working with food. Desks should be covered with plastic-coated fabric and cleaned with anti-bacterial spray before the work starts. Children should be reminded of the food hygiene and safety rules and as the products will be eaten, it is imperative that the children understand the importance of these. Emphasise them throughout the project.*

### Possible previous skills/knowledge needed

Children should be familiar with techniques of working with food. They should have analysed it and done taste-testing. They will also have used computer packages to produce and analyse questionnaires and have undertaken focused tasks covering the main aspects of designing and making.

### Key background information

In this activity, children will decide on a snack product which they would like to sell to other children in the school. They will devise a questionnaire to discover people's preferences and then design and make a snack. They will give it a name, a product identity, packaging and a poster campaign. Finally each group will present their product to the rest of the class in a short presentation, where samples of the snack will be available.

### Vocabulary

Marketing, product identity.

### Preparation

Ask each child to bring in a snack product ( a packet of crisps for example) for the start of the activity.

### Typical resources needed

Selection of simple recipe books and recipe cards, basic food ingredients (although children will make a list of requirements and this can be vetted to avoid any waste or undue expense), mixing bowls, plastic table cloths, protective clothing, kitchen utensils, baking trays, access to oven and microwave, oven gloves, paper, pencils, coloured felt-tipped pens, computers, desktop publishing and graphic software.

DESIGN AND
TECHNOLOGY

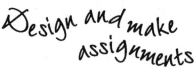
## What to do

As a class, discuss the wide range of snack products that are available. Use the samples that the children have brought in to illustrate the discussion. Talk about when snacks are eaten and why? Who eats them? Are sweet or savoury snacks most popular? How would you find out? Ask each group to devise a questionnaire that would give them some answers. They can publish it using a computer and then ask friends and family to fill it in. They can now analyse the questionnaire which should provide evidence to help them decide what sort of snack they should produce. Ask them to brainstorm some ideas in groups, and then share them as a whole class. The groups should now focus on the detail of their snack through research using recipe books and cards, and perhaps asking at home about simple recipes.

They should now produce a sketch of their idea showing the recipe they intend to use and what the packaging will look like. Discuss these ideas in detail with each group. When you consider the children have come up with some reasonable and practical ideas ask them to produce a plan of action and a list of ingredients and equipment that they will need. They should then be able to start making their snack. Emphasise the importance of quality and hygiene during the making process. They should evaluate the recipe themselves and then package it ready for the presentation, where the whole class will evaluate all the products. Provided appropriate care has been taken in terms of hygiene, this can include tasting.

## Suggestion(s) for extension

Some groups could set up taste-tests for their product and develop the snack further using the results of the evaluation which they receive. They could look particularly at issues such as its sweetness, stickiness, sickliness, and attractiveness.

## Opportunities for IT

The children might display their IT capability by using:
▲ a desktop publishing package to design and publish a questionnaire for the survey;
▲ a computer database to collate and analyse findings about a snack;
▲ graphing software to display the results of their survey;
▲ an art package to design packaging for their snack;
▲ a word processor or desktop publishing package to write and present a menu card/advertising poster for their snack;
▲ a word processor to write, edit and print an evaluation of their snack.

## Display ideas

The product, packaging and research will all be available for presentation at the end of the activity. This material can be wall-mounted either in the classroom or in the school entrance. On an open day, samples could be available for visitors.

# FAIRGROUND RIDES

*To choose appropriate electrical components, mechanisms and constructional materials in order to design and make a fairground ride.*

†† *Working in groups of four.*

🕐 *Four two-hour sessions.*

⚠ *Take care when using a saw and a hand-drill. When using a craft knife use a metal safety rule and a cutting mat. Closely supervise children using a soldering iron. Only use dry batteries as a source of electricity. Do not use rechargeable batteries as they can get very hot if short-circuited.*

## Possible previous skills/knowledge needed

Children should be familiar with a range of construction techniques and mechanisms. It is likely that they will have used electrical circuits, switches, motors and buzzers in models they have made. They will be familiar with using a construction kit as a prototyping tool and have undertaken focused tasks covering the main aspects of designing and making. This DMA is an ideal vehicle for children to develop their computer control work. This is included under 'Suggestion(s) for extension', but for a group of children who have extensive experience of using IT it could be set as part of the activity.

## Key background information

This activity will allow you to produce a fairground scene with a large number of working models. Children will be free to use a wide range of materials and will therefore have to justify their choices throughout the activity and at the end. A constraint will be the scale of the models. If the fairground is to look effective, they will all have to be the same scale. A small Plasticine figure given to each group will provide a reference point. The groups will also need to work well together and discuss their overall plan – you do not want five merry-go-rounds!

## Preparation

See if you can arrange a visit to a local fairground or theme park to start off the activity. Alternatively, make sure you have a lot of resource material available which contains pictures of fairground rides. Prepare a baseboard for the fairground to be built upon. This should incorporate papier mâché or Mod Roc undulations, fences and trees and be painted to look like an area of park land.

## Typical resources needed

LEDs, bulbs, bulb holders, wire, solder, soldering irons, paper-clips, drawing pins, batteries, battery holders, battery clips, motors, buzzers, selection of switches, small pieces of sheet metal, aluminium foil, cardboard, wood, foamboard, corrugated plastic, PVA adhesive, clear acetate sheet, scissors, wire

**DESIGN AND TECHNOLOGY**

cutters, saws, bench hooks, G-cramps, craft knives, metal safety rules, cutting mats, coat-hanger wire, pulleys, elastic bands, wooden wheels, dowel, paper and pencils.

## What to do

Show the children the area where they are going to build the model fairground. This will determine the scale of the individual models. Discuss the kinds of fairground rides that the children are familiar with. Use the resources available and/or remind them of their visit.

Each group of four should now work on two ideas. Rough sketches are all that are required at this stage. Lead a further class discussion to identify which ride each group will make. Further negotiation may be required to ensure that each group makes a substantially different ride. You also need to discuss scale, and each group should be given a Plasticine figure so that they know that this-sized person must fit into their ride. At this stage remind them of the skills and techniques that they could use – in particular, construction techniques and soldering.

Each group should produce a more detailed drawing of their idea showing materials and techniques they intend to use which you should discuss thoroughly. Ask detailed questions to see if the groups have actually made any decisions or just drawn what first came into their heads. When you consider the children have come up with some reasonable and practical ideas ask them to produce a plan of action and a list of materials and equipment that they will need. They should then be able to start making their fairground ride. Emphasise the importance of quality and continually remind them of the need for accuracy and care during construction.

## Suggestion(s) for extension

If some of the fairground rides include lighting and motors, it would be possible to control them using a computer. Lights could flash, roundabouts, for example, could revolve one way for 30 seconds, the other way for 30 seconds and then stop for 60 seconds. Children who wish to work on this extension need to have covered some of the more advanced activities in the chapter on 'Control'.

## Opportunities for IT

The children might display their IT capability by using:
▲ a drawing or CAD package to create a working design for their ride;
▲ computer control to control the movement of the ride such as the direction, speed or time, or other parts of the design such as flashing lights;
▲ an art or desktop publishing package to design and present a poster advertising their ride;
▲ a word processor to write, edit and print an evaluation of their fairground ride.

## Display ideas

The whole fairground forms a display which could easily provide a focal point in the main entrance hall of the school, particularly if elements of the model were computer controlled. A continuous tape of fairground noise and music could enhance the overall effect.

## STRING PUPPETS

*To identify a need for a puppet. To select appropriate materials to make a string puppet.*

†† *Working in groups of six for planning, individually when designing and making the puppet.*

🕐 *Five two-hour sessions.*

⚠ *Take care when using a saw and a hand-drill. Make sure that the children use a metal safety rule and a cutting mat when using a craft knife.*

## Possible previous skills/knowledge needed

Children should have made a product using papier mâché, used a saw and drilled pieces of wood, produced a pattern for clothes, and sewn and joined fabric. They will also have undertaken focused tasks which will have covered the main aspects of designing and making.

## Key background information

Making string puppets (or marionettes) is a popular activity and it lends itself well to a design and make assignment because there are so many choices that have to be made, and it usually requires children to use a wide range of materials. A typical scenario would be for a group of children to put on a puppet play, linked in some way to a topic they

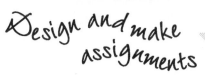
are studying in another area of the National Curriculum. The group has to decide the theme, write the play, select the characters, and put on the play. Individually they design and make their own puppet.

## Vocabulary
Marionette.

## Preparation
Find a range of resources on puppets for the children to use as reference material.

## Typical resources needed
Newspaper, tissue paper, wallpaper paste (without fungicide), Plasticine, brushes, selection of fabric, wood, saws, drills, drill bits, string, paint, scissors, pins, needles, thread, thin cord, G-cramps, bench hooks, craft knives, metal safety rules, cutting mats, paper and pencils.

## What to do
Explain that each group of six is going to produce a puppet play on a certain topic. The topic is likely to be one which is being covered in some other area of the curriculum. Although this is a very open-ended activity, there are certain constraints within which the children need to work. The puppets must be marionettes; there should be six characters in the play; they must all be made to the same scale. The children need to decide on the story of their play, identify the six characters they will make and decide on the relative sizes of the puppets. It is likely that the children will write their play in an English lesson rather than in a design and technology one.

At this stage remind the children of the skills and techniques they have learned while undertaking focused tasks which may be of use to them in this activity. Some which they should consider are:
▲ covering a Plasticine mould with papier mâché;
▲ using Mod Roc;
▲ cutting and drilling wood;
▲ finishing, using paint and varnish;
▲ making a paper pattern when working with fabric;
▲ sewing and decorating fabrics;
▲ making use of everyday items;
▲ packaging to provide particular shapes and textures.

Avoid showing the children too many examples of different puppets. It would be better to have a range of reference books on puppets which the children can use themselves. Try to extend their horizons further than a head, a body, two arms and two legs. Animals, monsters and creatures from outer space are just as appropriate, and will require different materials and techniques.

Children will now need to do sketches of their puppet and annotate them to show how they will be made. At this stage you should assist the children by asking questions and making constructive comments. Why did you choose

that material? Do you think it will be strong enough? I think it might be better to make that piece of wood a little longer and that hole a little smaller. It is important to remind children that all the puppets within one group must be constructed to the same scale and that they must be of a high quality. Once you are happy that they have considered most aspects of the design, they should produce a plan of work, and once you have approved that, they can start making their puppet. The puppets can then be used in a play which they have written in another area of the curriculum.

## Suggestion(s) for extension
There could be more strings to enhance the movement or there could be a moving mouth. If it is a robot, for example, it might have flashing lights incorporated within it. There are even 'trick' puppets, for example, a skeleton whose head can come off. There is also a need for the group to produce appropriate scenery for the puppet play – this can be undertaken as a group activity while others are completing their own puppets. Encourage the children to look in the puppet resource books and come up with more sophisticated ideas.

## Opportunities for IT
The children might display their IT capability by using:
▲ a drawing or CAD package to design a pattern for the puppet's clothes';
▲ use a word processor or desktop publishing package to write and present the script for their play;
▲ a word processor to write, edit and print an evaluation of their puppet.

## Display ideas
The puppet show which the children put on using their own puppets is the focus for this whole activity. A video recording of the performance could be made which could be played back on a TV screen surrounded by the puppets. This would provide an excellent display for a parents' evening or governors' meeting.

**DESIGN AND TECHNOLOGY**

# Photocopiables

The pages in this section can be photocopied for use in the classroom or school which has purchased this book, and do not need to be declared in any return in respect of any photocopying licence.

They comprise a varied selection of both pupil and teacher resources, including pupil worksheets, resource material and record sheets to be completed by the teacher or children. Most of the photocopiable pages are related to individual activities in the book; the name of the activity is indicated at the top of the sheet, together with a page reference indicating where the lesson plan for that activity can be found.

Individual pages are discussed in detail within each lesson plan, accompanied by ideas for adaptation where appropriate – of course, each sheet can be adapted to suit your own needs and those of your class. Sheets can also be coloured, laminated, mounted on to card, enlarged and so on where appropriate.

Pupil worksheets and record sheets have spaces provided for children's names and for noting the date on which each sheet was used. This means that, if so required, they can be included easily within any pupil assessment portfolio.

**Flat packaging (see page 14)**

## Shell structures

**DESIGN AND TECHNOLOGY**

**Flat packaging (see page 14)**

## Mystery package one

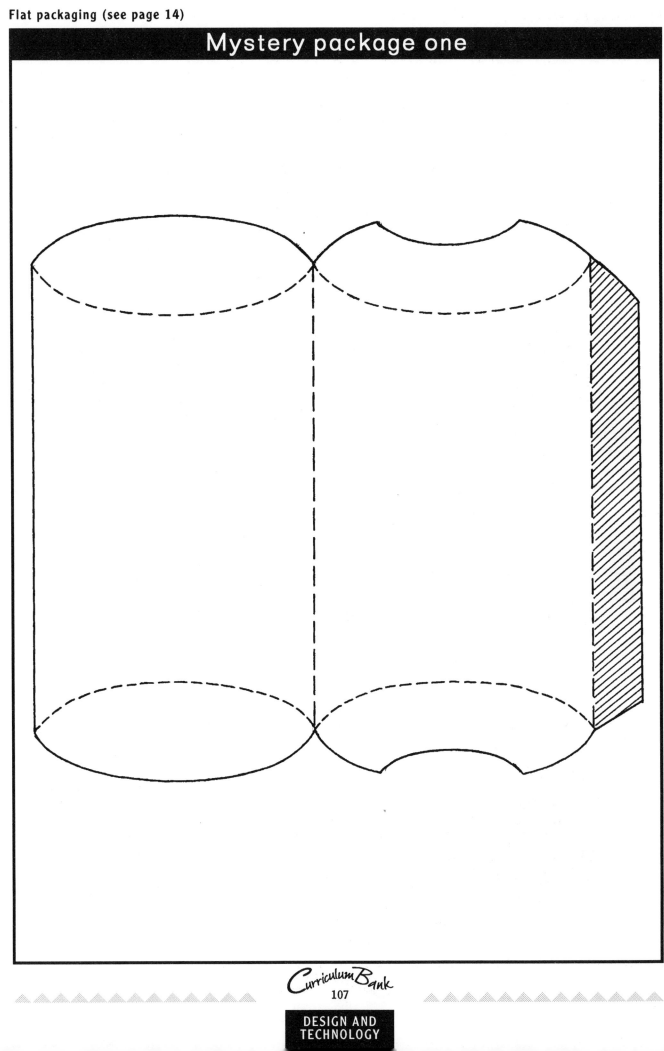

**DESIGN AND TECHNOLOGY**

**Flat packaging (see page 14)**

## Mystery package two

▲ Open up the pack, then 'click' the top over. The bottom can be glued if you wish.

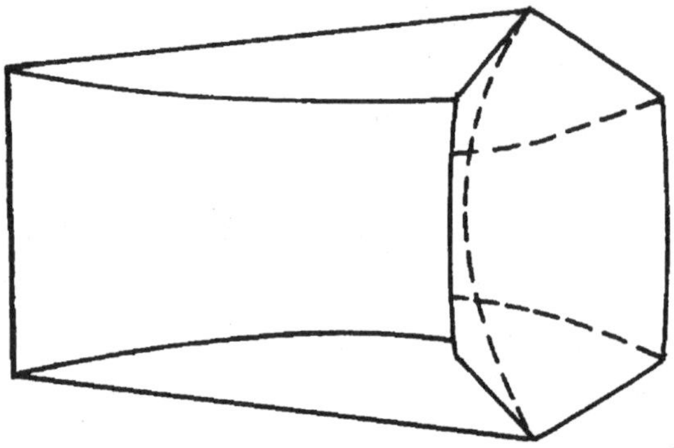

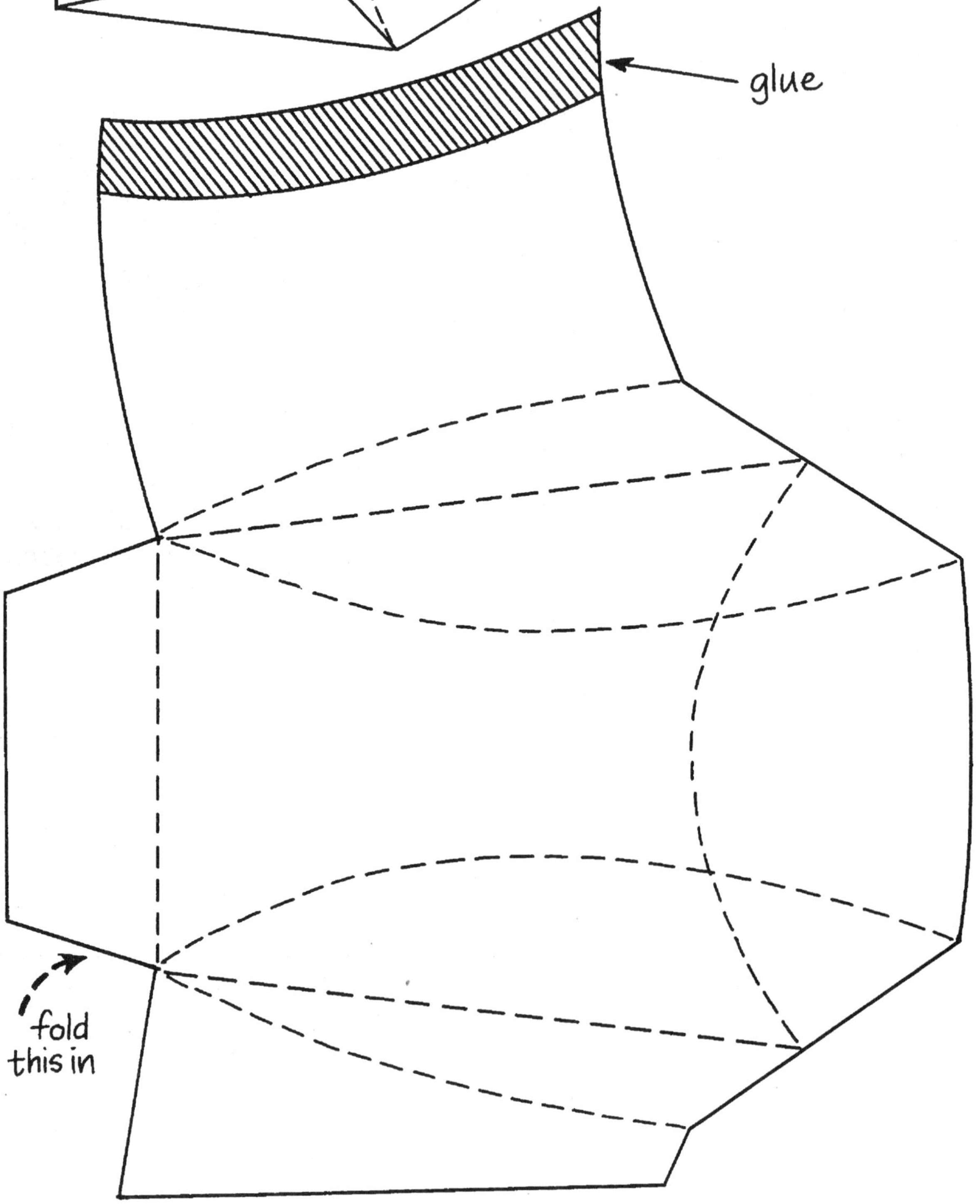

glue

fold this in

**DESIGN AND TECHNOLOGY**

**Beams (see page 15)**

## An investigation into beams

Name _____  Date _____

▲ Put two piles of books about 15cm apart on your desk.

▲ Now, using one sheet of A4 paper each time, see how you can fold it so that it will hold the largest weight. You may use a little adhesive if you need to. Below are some suggestions for ways to fold your paper. You could try others.

▲ Draw your ideas for paper beams on a separate sheet of paper. Remember – only use one sheet of paper per beam.

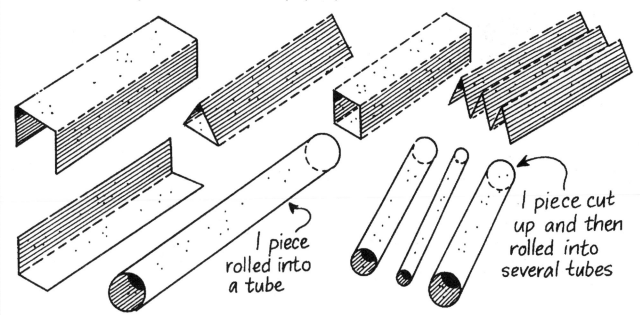

I piece rolled into a tube

I piece cut up and then rolled into several tubes

▲ When you have finished this investigation write down two things that are important so that you make a strong beam.

<br>

<br>

**DESIGN AND TECHNOLOGY**

**Beam bridge (see page 17)**

# Template for a beam bridge

(This template is drawn to half scale. If it is photocopied at 200% enlargement you will have a template for a bridge 30cm long and approximately 10cm high.)

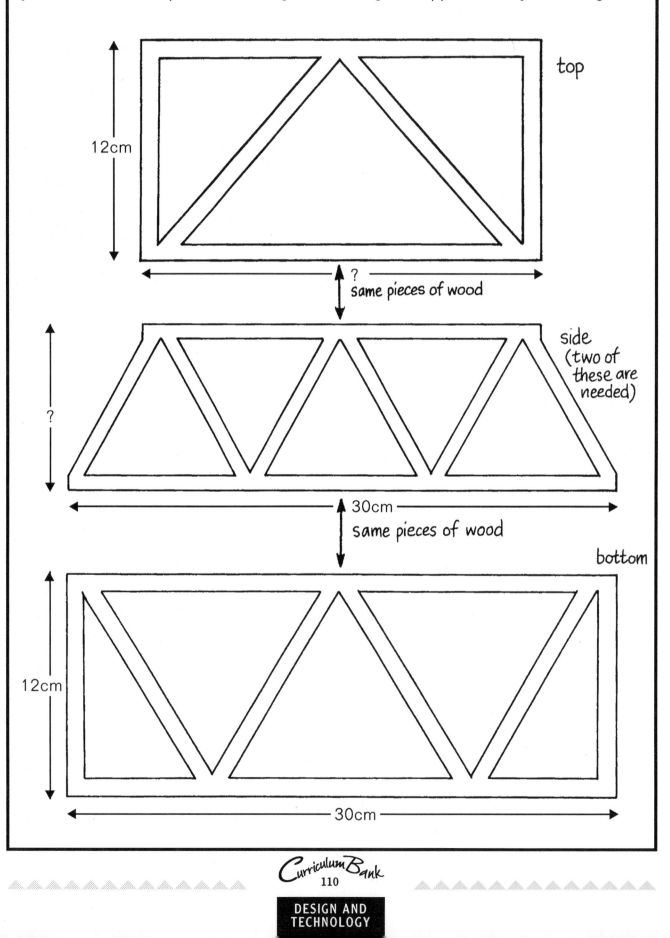

**DESIGN AND TECHNOLOGY**

Geodesics (see page 18)

## Making a geodesic building

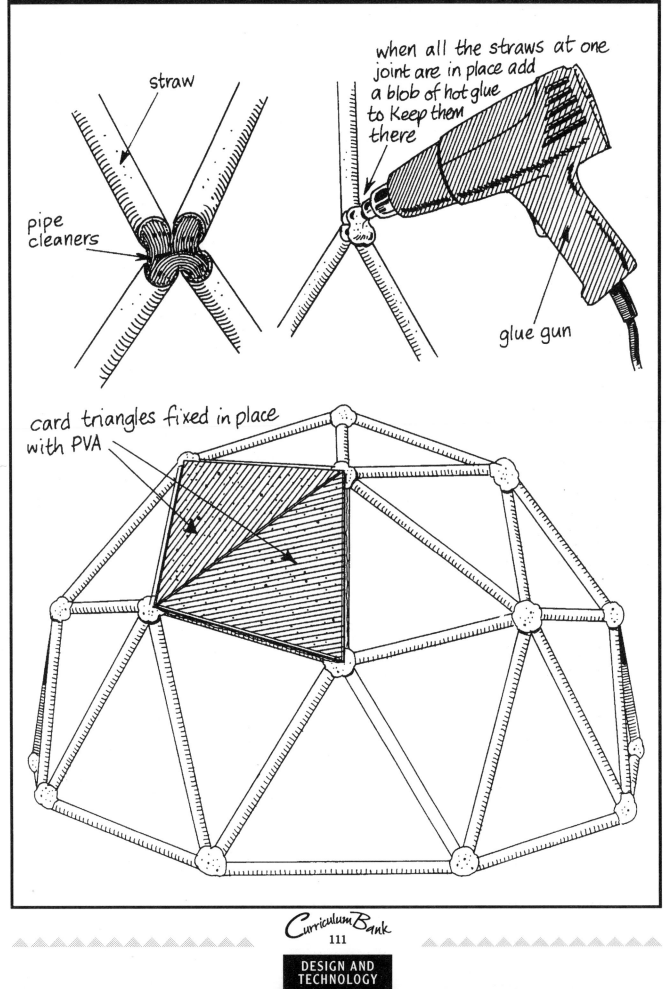

straw

pipe cleaners

when all the straws at one joint are in place add a blob of hot glue to keep them there

glue gun

card triangles fixed in place with PVA

DESIGN AND TECHNOLOGY

**Obstacle course (see page 20)**

# How to make paper tube structures

▲ Roll up the sheet of paper tightly around the wooden dowel. Use the head of a spoon to press down very firmly along the join. If the ends of the roll are not straight, trim them until they are.

If you want the tube to be coloured, you need decorate only one end of the paper – all the rest is rolled up and hidden.

▲ Flatten both ends of the tube, and make a hole using a paper punch or a paper drill. Fix the ends together using brass paper fasteners.

wooden dowel

glue

press head of spoon firmly along the join

paper

flattened

punch hole using heavy duty punch

cut off ends if they are not straight

brass paper fastener

all these are tubes

tent-shaped structure

DESIGN AND TECHNOLOGY

**Making a Tudor building (see page 21)**

## Types of Tudor building

DESIGN AND
TECHNOLOGY

**Making a Tudor building (see page 21)**

# A Tudor cottage

▲ Enlarge this sheet to produce a template of an appropriate size.

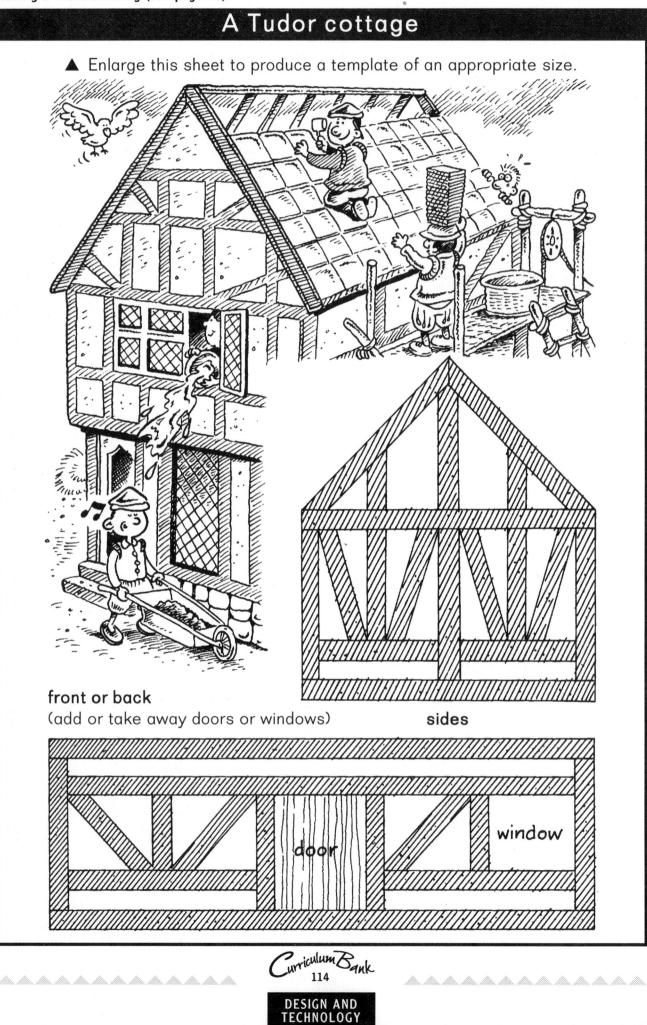

**front or back**
(add or take away doors or windows)

**sides**

door

window

**DESIGN AND TECHNOLOGY**

**Making a Tudor building (see page 21)**

## Tudor building planning sheet

Name _____     Date _____

Type of building _____

Dimensions     height _____

width _____

depth _____

Plan of front

Plan of back

Plan of sides

**DESIGN AND TECHNOLOGY**

# Evaluating toys

Name _____ Date _____

| |
|---|
| What shape is it? |
| What does it feel like? |
| What is it made of? |
| What materials might we use to make it today? |
| How is it made? |
| By hand or machine? |
| What tools would be needed? |
| Does it move? |
| What makes it move? |
| Does it make a noise? |
| Who would play with it? |
| Where and when? |
| Is it more fun to play with if it costs a lot? |
| Is it played with by boys and girls? |
| What aged children will play with it? |
| Is it safe? (CE mark) |
| Does it need a battery? |
| Your questions |

**DESIGN AND TECHNOLOGY**

**A pneumatic car park barrier (see page 25)**

# An investigation into pneumatics

▲ Put your finger over the end of the syringe.
Press hard on the plunger.
Describe what happens.

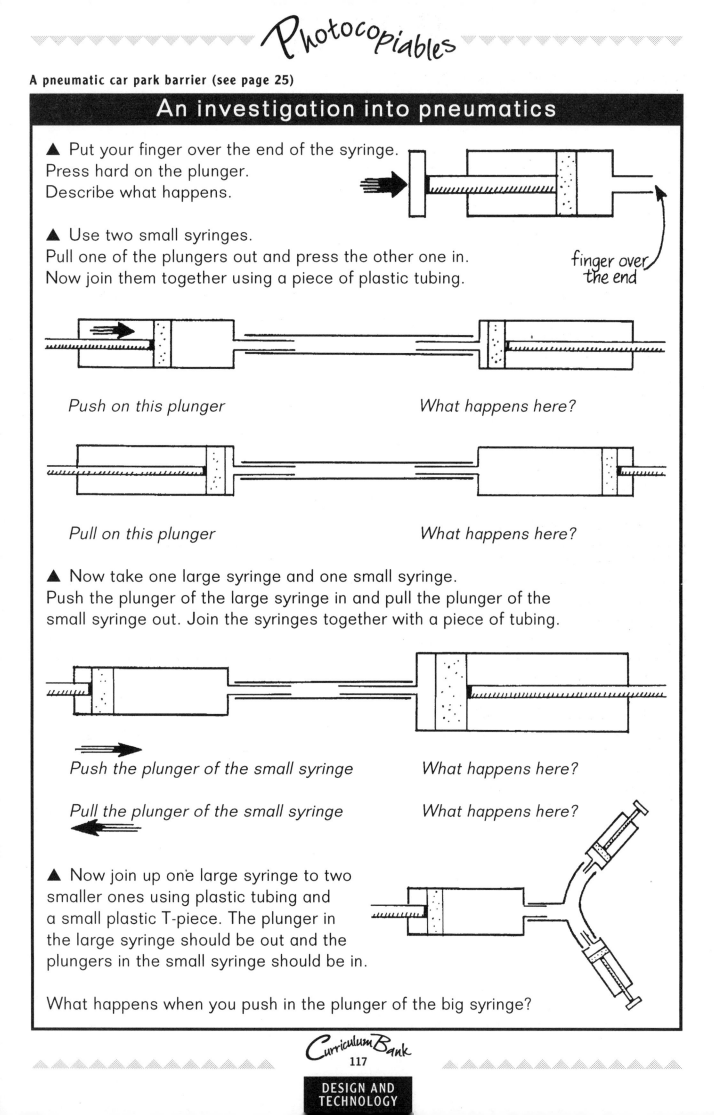

*finger over the end*

▲ Use two small syringes.
Pull one of the plungers out and press the other one in.
Now join them together using a piece of plastic tubing.

*Push on this plunger*                    *What happens here?*

*Pull on this plunger*                     *What happens here?*

▲ Now take one large syringe and one small syringe.
Push the plunger of the large syringe in and pull the plunger of the
small syringe out. Join the syringes together with a piece of tubing.

*Push the plunger of the small syringe*       *What happens here?*

*Pull the plunger of the small syringe*        *What happens here?*

▲ Now join up one large syringe to two
smaller ones using plastic tubing and
a small plastic T-piece. The plunger in
the large syringe should be out and the
plungers in the small syringe should be in.

What happens when you push in the plunger of the big syringe?

**DESIGN AND TECHNOLOGY**

A pneumatic car park barrier (see page 25)

## An annotated presentation drawing

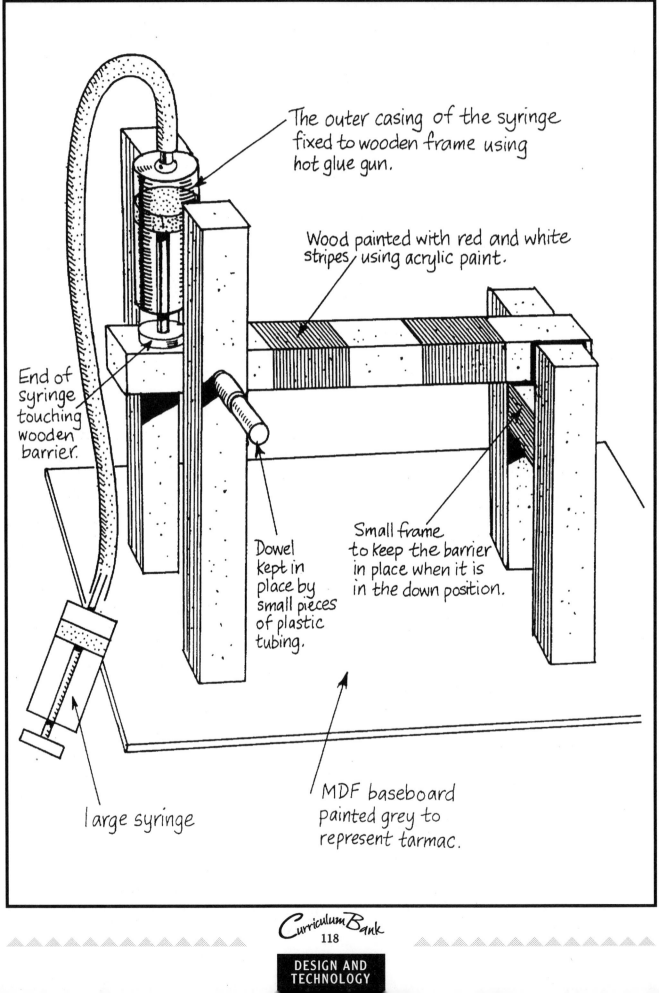

The outer casing of the syringe fixed to wooden frame using hot glue gun.

Wood painted with red and white stripes, using acrylic paint.

End of syringe touching wooden barrier.

Dowel kept in place by small pieces of plastic tubing.

Small frame to keep the barrier in place when it is in the down position.

large syringe

MDF baseboard painted grey to represent tarmac.

DESIGN AND TECHNOLOGY

**An advertising toy (see page 27)**

## What are cams?

The follower moves easily in the guide.

As the cam turns round the follower moves up and down.

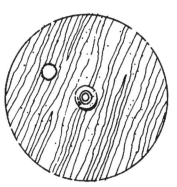

guide

dowel

follower

pear-shaped cam

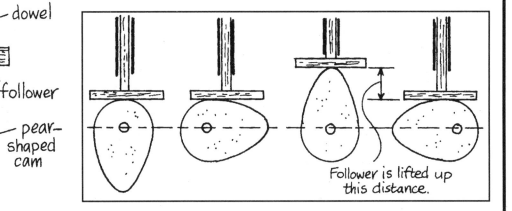

Follower is lifted up this distance.

### Circular off-centred cam

The follower is always moving up and down.

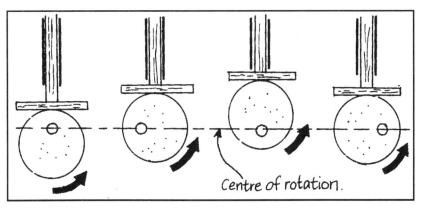

Centre of rotation.

▲ Make a cam using a wooden wheel and drill a hole off centre.

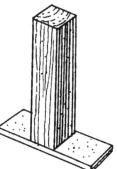

▲ Make a follower from a piece of square-section wood and a rectangle of foamboard.

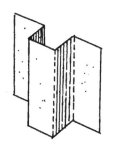

The guide can be made from folded card –

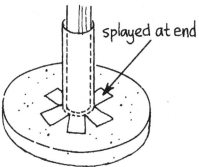

splayed at end

OR you can use another wheel and a piece of dowel and using a Jumbo art straw as a guide.

**An advertising toy (see page 27)**

# Using cams in models

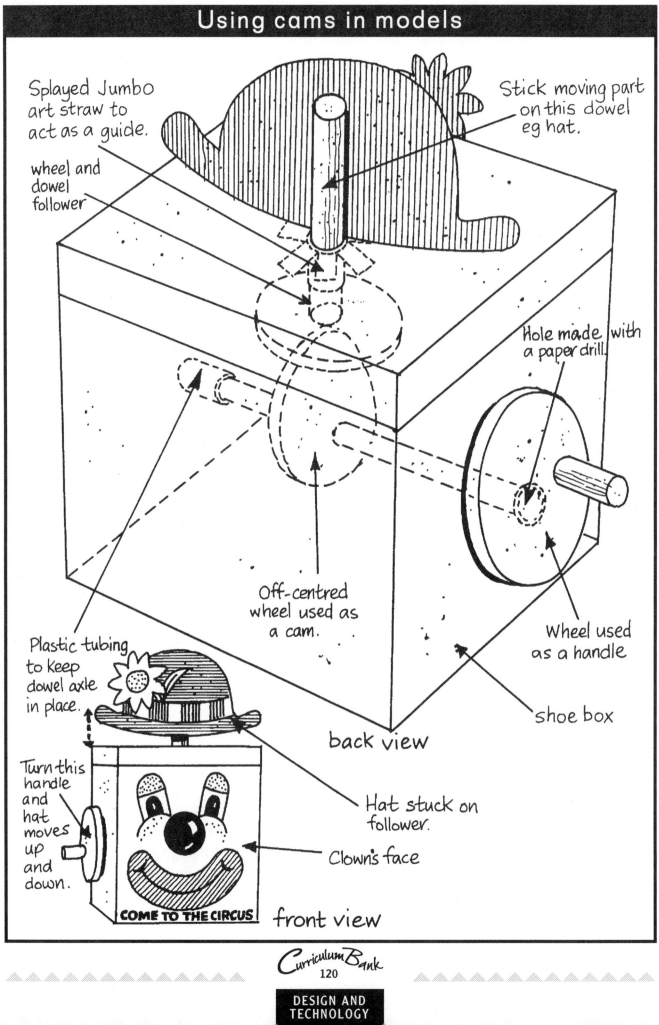

Splayed Jumbo art straw to act as a guide.

wheel and dowel follower

Stick moving part on this dowel eg hat.

Hole made with a paper drill.

Off-centred wheel used as a cam.

Wheel used as a handle

shoe box

back view

Plastic tubing to keep dowel axle in place.

Turn this handle and hat moves up and down.

Hat stuck on follower.

Clown's face

COME TO THE CIRCUS

front view

DESIGN AND
TECHNOLOGY

The cow jumped over the moon! (see page 29)

# The cow jumped over the moon

▲ Stick the picture of the cow onto a piece of foamboard. Use spray adhesive, but do not use too much. Make sure you place the picture near the edge of the sheet so as not to waste any material unnecessarily.

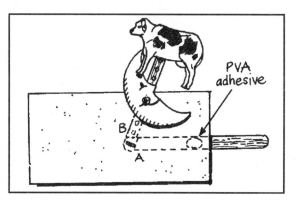

▲ Do the same with the picture of the moon. When the pictures are stuck firmly, use the shaper saw to cut round the outlines.

▲ Using a paper drill, carefully make a small hole about 5cm from the top of a piece of foamboard 20cm by 10cm (the base). Put a brass paper fastener through the hole to the back.

▲ Make a dent in the back of the foamboard which has the moon on it, using the paper drill. Stick the moon onto the base foamboard using PVA adhesive, so that the dent you have made goes over the head of the brass paper fastener (and hides it!).

▲ Stick two lolly sticks together using PVA adhesive and leave 10 minutes to dry. Cover the lolly sticks with a water-based varnish. Do one side first, let it dry, then do the other. Now do this again with another pair of lolly sticks.

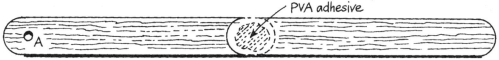

▲ Using a heavy-duty hole punch, make one hole at the end of one pair of lolly sticks (A), and a series of holes, equally spaced, along the length of the second pair (B). Mark them first with a pencil.

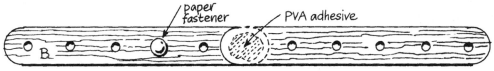

▲ Join (A) to (B) using a brass paper fastener. Stick the back of the cow onto the free end of B using PVA adhesive. Fix the brass paper fastener which is sticking out of the back of the base through one of the free holes in B.

▲ Move the free end of A backwards and forwards and the cow jumps over the moon. If you put the brass paper fastener in the hole on B farthest away from the cow, it moves a much greater distance. If you change it to a hole much nearer the cow, it hardly moves at all!

DESIGN AND
TECHNOLOGY

**Gear wheels (see page 30)**

# How to make simple gear wheels

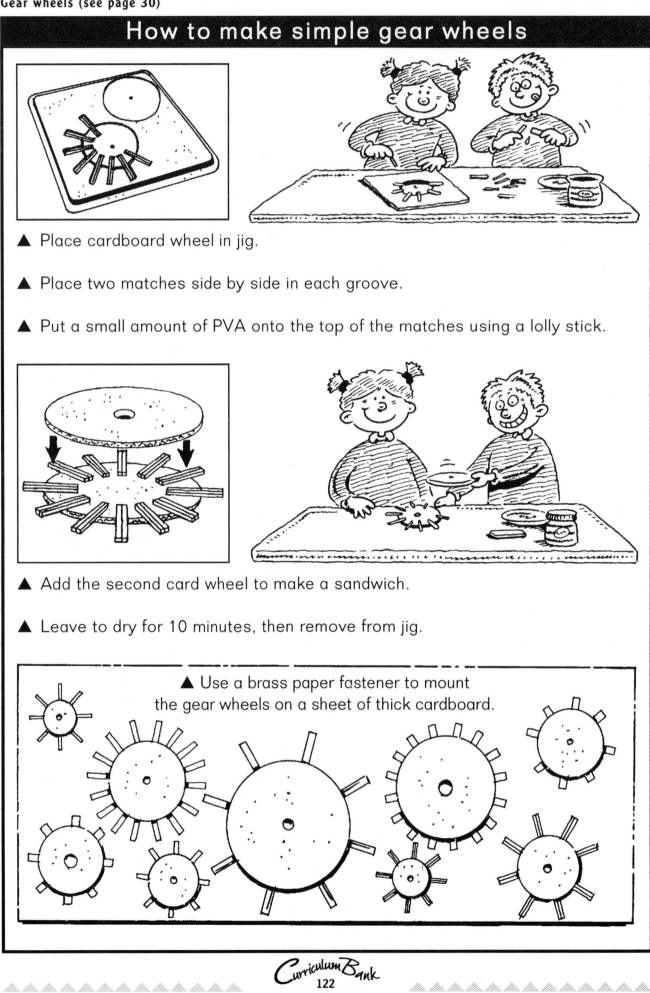

▲ Place cardboard wheel in jig.

▲ Place two matches side by side in each groove.

▲ Put a small amount of PVA onto the top of the matches using a lolly stick.

▲ Add the second card wheel to make a sandwich.

▲ Leave to dry for 10 minutes, then remove from jig.

▲ Use a brass paper fastener to mount
the gear wheels on a sheet of thick cardboard.

**DESIGN AND
TECHNOLOGY**

Gear wheels (see page 30)

# An investigation into gears

Name _____ Date _____

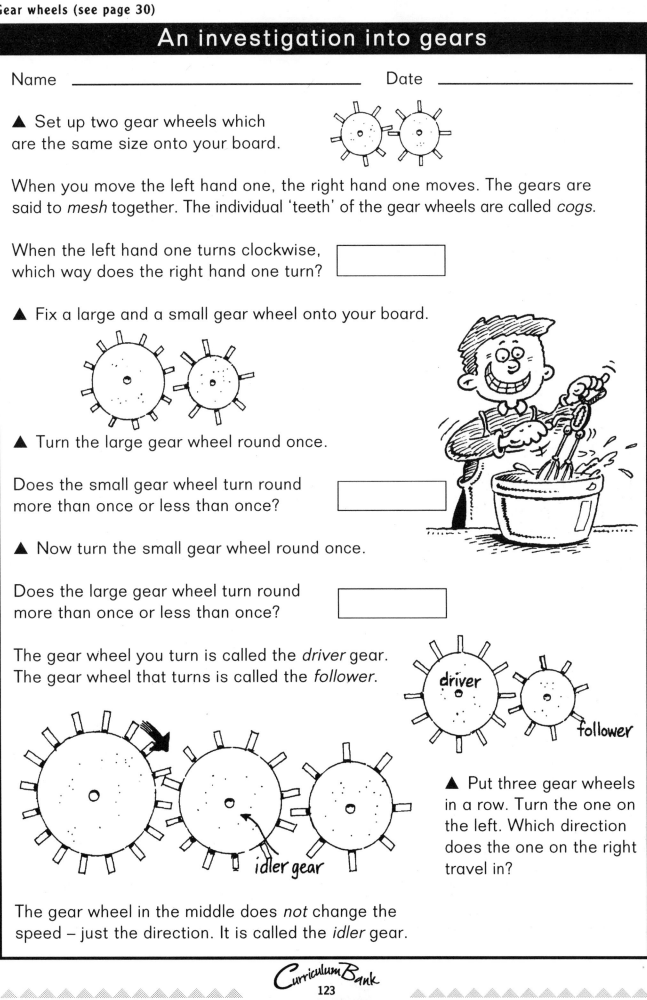

▲ Set up two gear wheels which are the same size onto your board.

When you move the left hand one, the right hand one moves. The gears are said to *mesh* together. The individual 'teeth' of the gear wheels are called *cogs*.

When the left hand one turns clockwise, which way does the right hand one turn?

▲ Fix a large and a small gear wheel onto your board.

▲ Turn the large gear wheel round once.

Does the small gear wheel turn round more than once or less than once?

▲ Now turn the small gear wheel round once.

Does the large gear wheel turn round more than once or less than once?

The gear wheel you turn is called the *driver* gear. The gear wheel that turns is called the *follower*.

driver

follower

▲ Put three gear wheels in a row. Turn the one on the left. Which direction does the one on the right travel in?

idler gear

The gear wheel in the middle does *not* change the speed – just the direction. It is called the *idler* gear.

A zoetrope (see page 31)

# Making a zoetrope

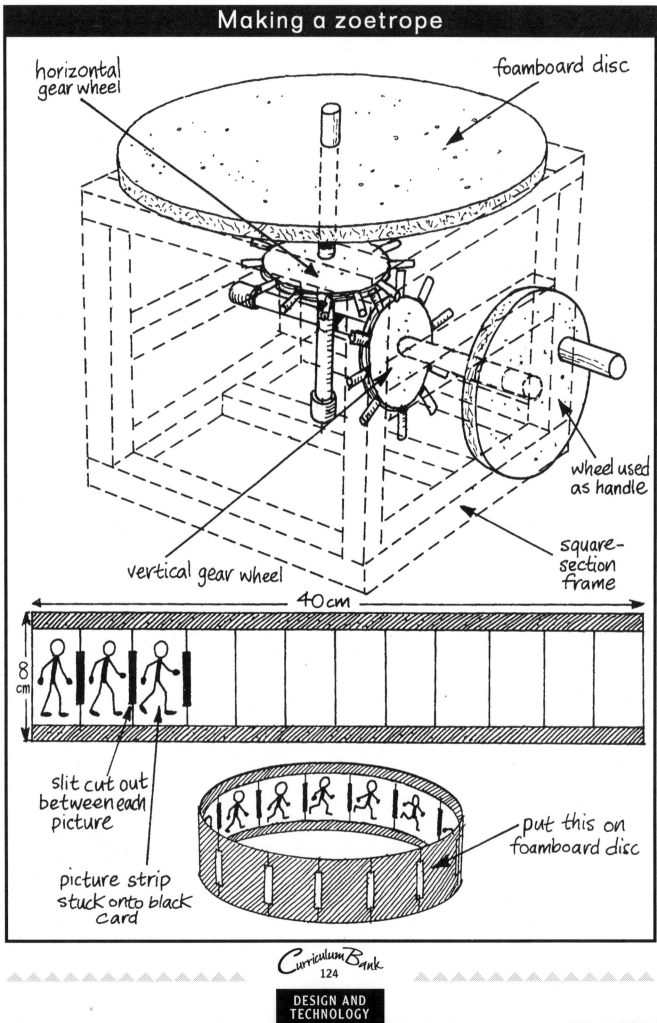

horizontal gear wheel

foamboard disc

wheel used as handle

square-section frame

vertical gear wheel

40cm

8cm

slit cut out between each picture

picture strip stuck onto black card

put this on foamboard disc

DESIGN AND TECHNOLOGY

**A conveyor belt (see page 33)**

# Suggestions for pulley wheels

Cotton reels

Drinks cans with dowel-sized holes drilled through both ends

Two wooden wheels with card rolled round to make the pulley wide like a conveyor belt

Use a cardboard tube and seal up the ends with card, wood, plastic pulleys and/or wheels

Plastic pulley wheels with elastic bands as drive belts

Twisted band reverses the direction

A conveyor belt (see page 33)

# Making a conveyor belt

▲ Make the conveyor belt track first.
Then it can be fitted tightly to the pulleys as the framework is being built.

▲ Cut out length of corrugated cardboard. Measure accurately.

2 flat edges stuck with PVA.
Squeeze tightly.

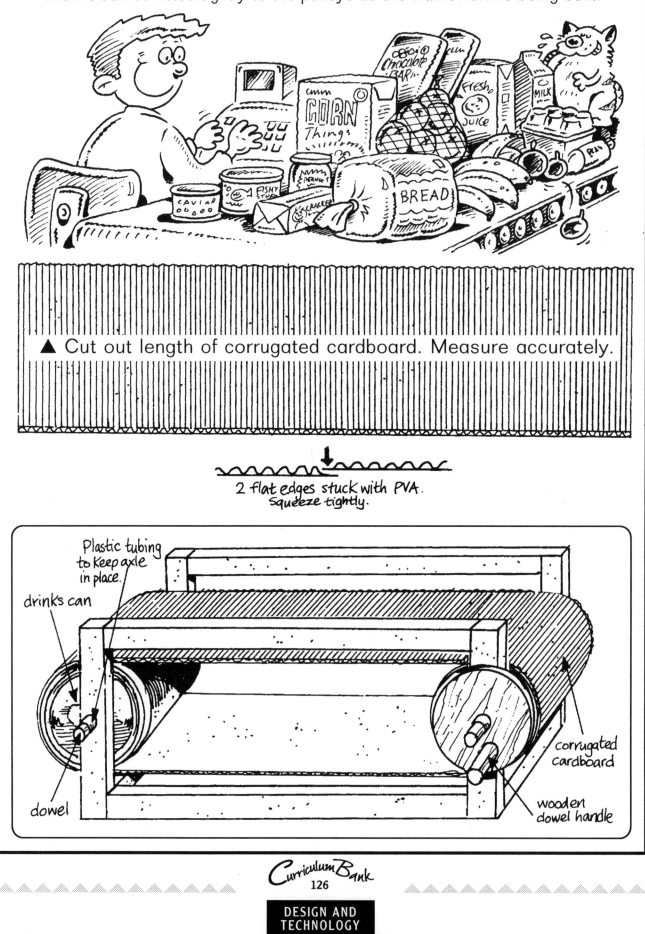

DESIGN AND
TECHNOLOGY

**An energy map of the school (see page 36)**

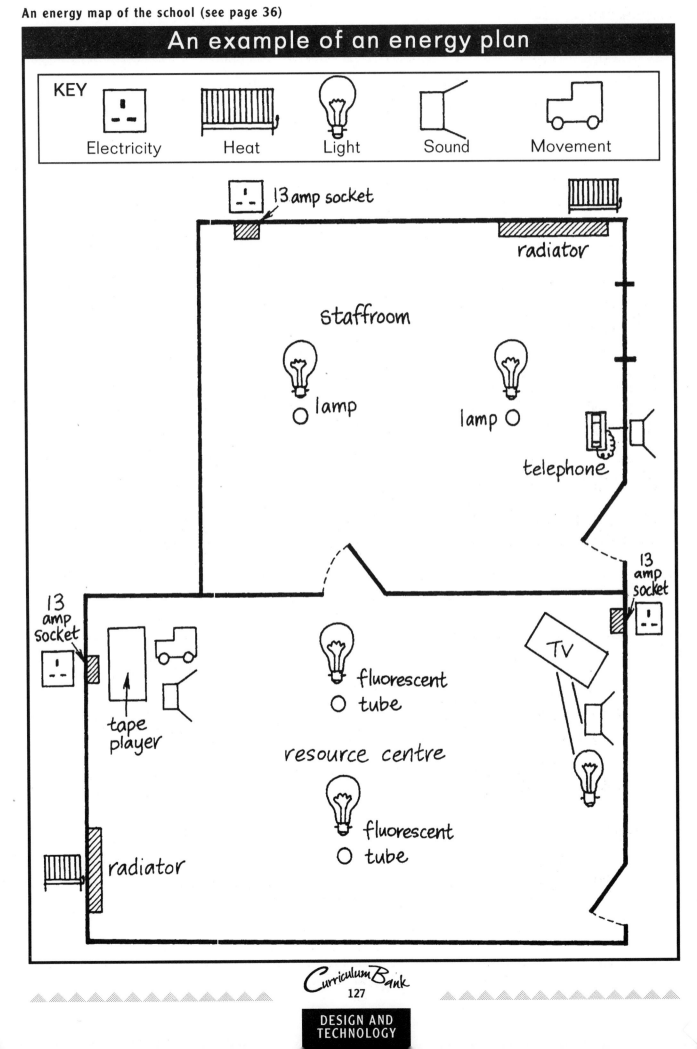

## An example of an energy plan

KEY — Electricity · Heat · Light · Sound · Movement

13 amp socket

radiator

staffroom

lamp      lamp

telephone

13 amp socket

13 amp socket

tape player

fluorescent tube

TV

resource centre

fluorescent tube

radiator

Water power (see page 38)

# What is water power?

## Water-wheels

Water-wheels were used to turn machinery. There are two types – the overshot, where the weight of the water falling turns the wheel and the undershot, where the weight of the water pushing causes the wheel to turn.

## Hydroelectricity

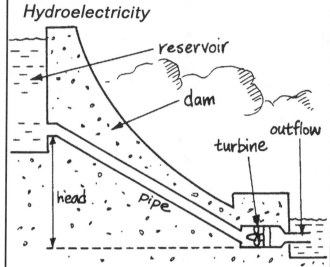

The dam holds back large amounts of water. Then the water is allowed to flow through pipes in the dam and through a turbine. Large areas have to be flooded to provide the large reservoirs. Small hydroelectric schemes for small groups of people are now available both in this country and abroad.

## Tidal power

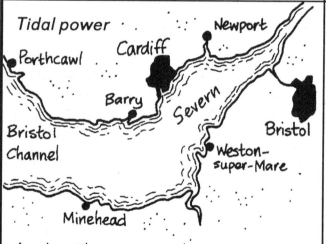

As the tide comes in there is a great deal of force which can be used to turn water turbines. Then the water can be trapped behind the dam and later turn the turbine again as it returns to the sea. Possibilities in this country include the Severn estuary, but there are great concerns about the effect on wildlife in the area.

## Wave power

As the waves move up and down, Salter's Ducks wobble up and down and this movement can be used to make electricity. The Salter's Ducks need to be in very rough water, so that there are lots of waves but this means that they can be easily damaged and there are difficulties in getting the electricity to the shore where it is needed.

**DESIGN AND TECHNOLOGY**

**Water power (see page 38)**

# The presentation

These are some of the jobs that need to be done so that the presentation is clear, useful and interesting. Each of you in the group needs to work hard to make the group's presentation successful.

## Task 1 | Someone needs to organise the group

This does not mean 'bossing people around', but it does mean seeing that everyone is working on some part of the presentation, and that everyone knows what everyone else is doing.

## Task 2 | Writing the words

You might decide to write a script which you will read, or you might choose to do a short play. If you use a word-processing program you can print out the words in a very large font so that they are easy to see.

## Task 3 | Drawing the pictures

It is often said that a picture is worth a thousand words. If you try to describe someone's face to the rest of the group they would still not really know what they looked like. Therefore, use as many picture resources as you can (you could use clip art that you find on many computers) including your own drawings if you wish.

## Task 4 | How can you make the presentation really interesting?

How can you make everyone remember your presentation and the things that you said? Try a short piece of drama, or get everyone in the group to talk rather than just one or two speakers.

## Task 5 | Research from books, brochures, magazines, CD-ROMs and videos

Photocopiable sheet 128 gives you just a small amount of information about obtaining energy from water. You will need to find a great deal more from resources which you have in the classroom, in the library or at home. CD-ROM programs often include sound, animations or clips of film which you may be able to use.

## Task 6 | Building simple models to help explain ideas

Sometimes it is much easier to explain if you have a model in front of you to show how something really works. You may decide that it would be useful to have or make a model for your presentation.

Getting water to do work (see page 40)

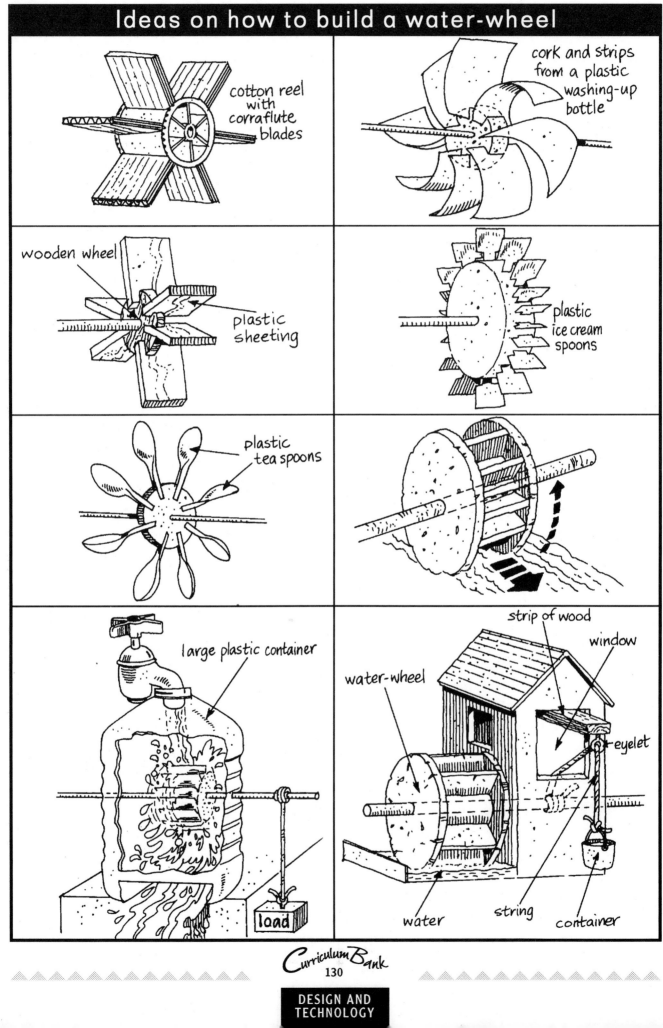

## Ideas on how to build a water-wheel

cotton reel with corraflute blades

cork and strips from a plastic washing-up bottle

wooden wheel

plastic sheeting

plastic ice cream spoons

plastic tea spoons

large plastic container

load

strip of wood

window

water-wheel

eyelet

water

string

container

DESIGN AND TECHNOLOGY

**Wind energy (see page 41)**

# Energy from the wind

People in Egypt, China, Babylon, Persia and other ancient civilisations were using the power of the wind to help them do some of their work over 5000 years ago. Windmills and wind pumps were commonly found in Great Britain right up to the beginning of this century. Their main use was in grinding corn and pumping water. They usually did the same amount of work as 200 people could do. In many countries the wind is still used extensively for pumping water.

Wind machines designed to do mechanical work should be quite solid-looking such as the Savonius water pump and the multiblade wind pump.

Savonius water pump

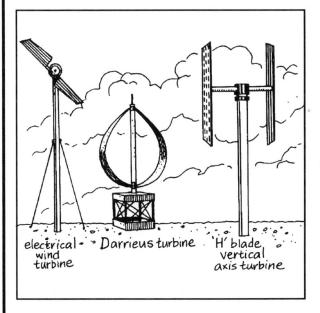

electrical wind turbine · Darrieus turbine · 'H' blade vertical axis turbine

Nowadays wind is more likely to be used to make electricity. This only happened because in the 1970s people realised that coal, oil and gas would not last forever and that we needed to look at other ways of making electricity. In Great Britain in 1995 there were over 450 large wind turbines which can produce enough electricity for 250 000 people.

Wind machines designed to make electricity need to go much more quickly and they are less solid, having small blades such as the electrical wind turbine, Darrieus and 'H' blade turbines.

Remember, there are problems with windmills and wind turbines. In order to turn, the sails have to face into the wind, but the wind does not always blow in the same direction, so the sails have to be able to move into the wind. On some wind machines there is a tail fin which means that the wind will hit the fin, making the top of the wind machine twist so that the sails are facing into the wind. On some machines this is done by hand.

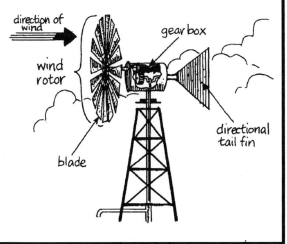

direction of wind

gear box

wind rotor

directional tail fin

blade

DESIGN AND TECHNOLOGY

Wind energy (see page 41)

# Energy from the wind

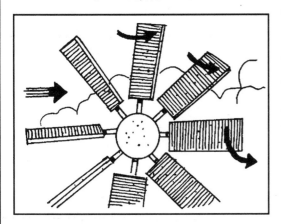

When the wind blows really hard the blades spin faster and faster and it is possible that they could be damaged. They can be designed to make the blades twist so that some of the wind does not hit the blades at all and escapes.

Blades twist round so that wind can pass right through if it becomes too strong. This means that the wind rotor slows down preventing damage.

It is very important that wind machines are built in the right place. There needs to be a lot of wind and, therefore, they need to be on a hillside rather than in a valley. They also need to be well away from people's houses as they make quite a noise and can be very large. There have been some experiments with wind machines being built right out at sea. This is because there is a lot of wind there, and they do not interfere with people's lives. However, it is much more expensive to build them out at sea.

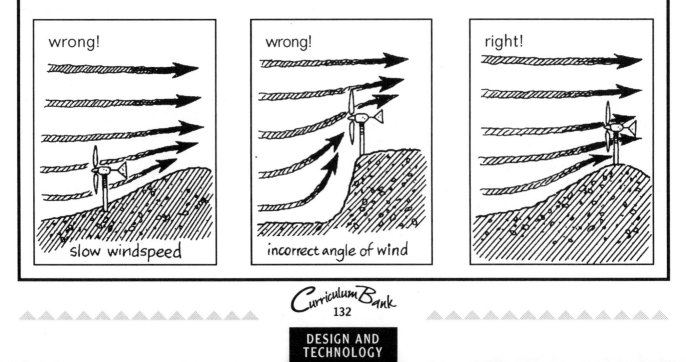

DESIGN AND TECHNOLOGY

**Wind energy (see page 41)**

## Questions about energy from the wind

**1** Name some of the countries where wind has been used as a source of energy.

**2** Give two examples of ways in which wind can be used to help us.

**3** If you wanted to make a wind machine that would produce electricity, what kind of blade could you use?

**4** You have to choose whether to build a very large wind turbine or quite a small one. Which would you build, and explain why?

**5** You need to choose where to build your wind turbine. What sorts of places would you choose? Where would you *not* build it?

**6** Why do we now use the wind to make electricity for us instead of using it to turn machinery?

**7** Do you think the wind will give us more of our energy in the future? Why?

**8** Carry out some research, then draw two different wind machines used in two different countries.

**9** Using resource materials, research why there are very few working windmills in Great Britain today.

**10** Discover through research why it is impossible for us to get all our electricity from wind machines.

**DESIGN AND TECHNOLOGY**

**Travelling towards the wind (see page 42)**

## A vehicle that travels towards the wind

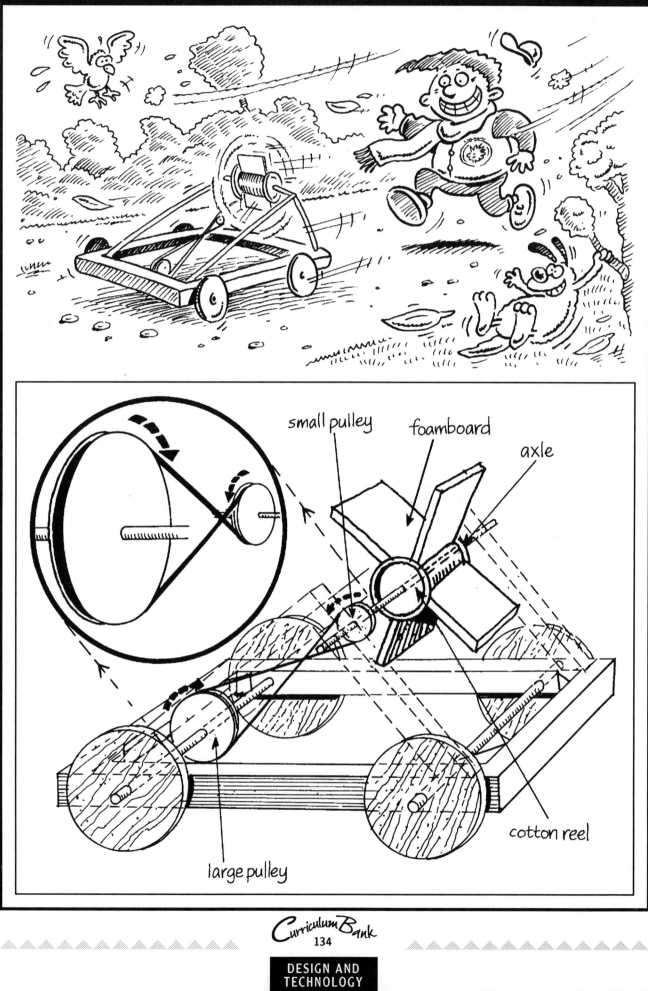

small pulley

foamboard

axle

cotton reel

large pulley

**DESIGN AND TECHNOLOGY**

**A propeller-powered boat (see page 44)**

# Important things to consider

Use a plastic container?

margarine tub

Or build your own?

wooden sides of boat – use waterproof glue

pointed shape

make sides of the boat high enough

dimensions – will it fit inside the guttering?

propeller – does it hit the boat?

battery holder – make sure weight of motor and batteries balance

framework for motor

sheet of corraflute

DESIGN AND TECHNOLOGY

**A hovercraft (see page 45)**

## A simple hovercraft

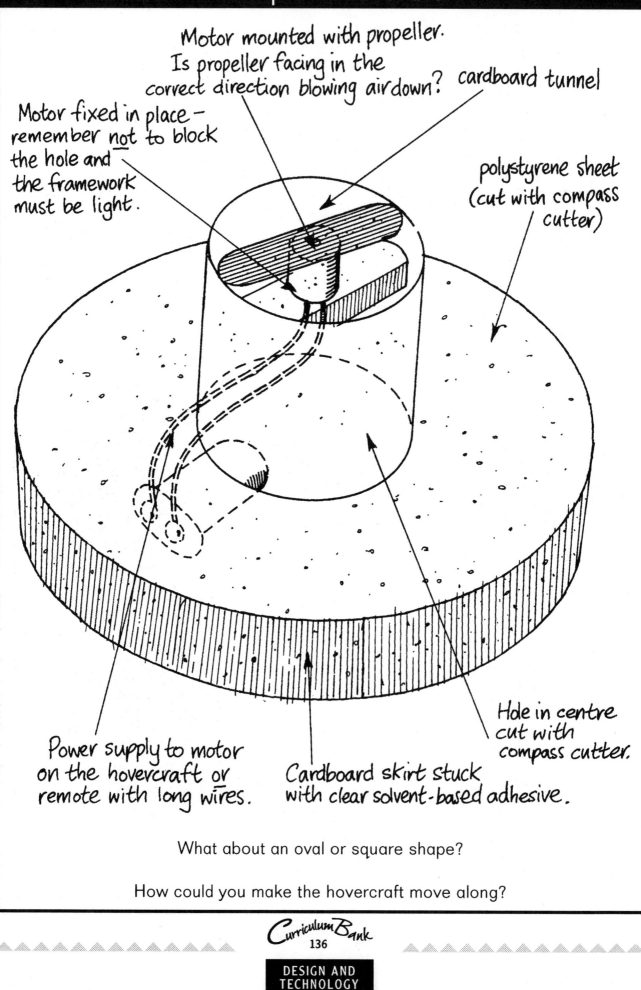

Motor mounted with propeller.
Is propeller facing in the
correct direction blowing air down?

cardboard tunnel

Motor fixed in place —
remember **not** to block
the hole and
the framework
must be light.

polystyrene sheet
(cut with compass
cutter)

Hole in centre
cut with
compass cutter.

Power supply to motor
on the hovercraft or
remote with long wires.

Cardboard skirt stuck
with clear solvent-based adhesive.

What about an oval or square shape?

How could you make the hovercraft move along?

**DESIGN AND TECHNOLOGY**

**Musical maracas (see page 48)**

# Making some maracas

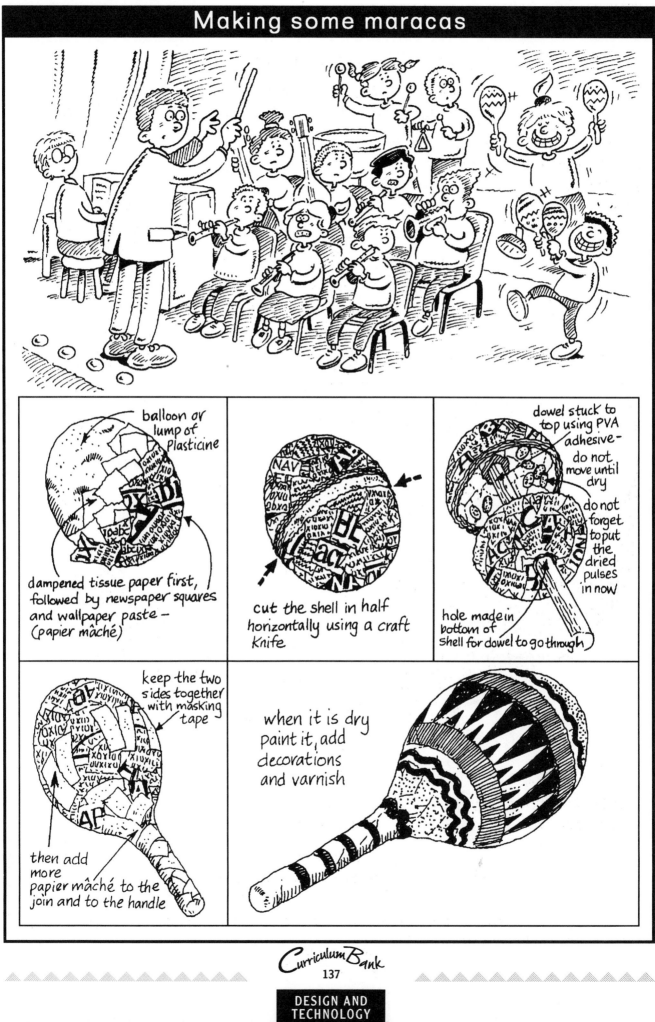

balloon or lump of Plasticine

dampened tissue paper first, followed by newspaper squares and wallpaper paste – (papier mâché)

cut the shell in half horizontally using a craft knife

dowel stuck to top using PVA adhesive – do not move until dry

do not forget to put the dried pulses in now

hole made in bottom of shell for dowel to go through

keep the two sides together with masking tape

then add more papier mâché to the join and to the handle

when it is dry paint it, add decorations and varnish

**Plastazote for protection (see page 51)**

# Working with Plastazote

cut with scissors · craft knife · metal safety rule · cutting mat

hold onto suitable shape until cool

lace up or Velcro · hot-glue gun · punch holes or Velcro (use eyelets to strengthen the holes)

You can emboss the material by pressing shapes into the warm surface. Press down using a flat board to stick two surfaces together.

The material can be sewn.

**Dough plaques (see page 54)**

## Working with bread dough

this animal shape is made of
pieces of dough stuck together

a sharp instrument can be
used to make marks in the dough

put dough through a mincer
or garlic press to give this hair effect

twist of dough
to form
handle

large
plaited
loaf

simple roll -
ball of dough with
cross        on top

use a fork
to texture
the basket

twist of dough to form base

**DESIGN AND TECHNOLOGY**

**Mod Roc masks (see page 55)**

# How to use Mod Roc

▲ Cover up the work surface with sheets of old newspaper. Wear appropriate protective clothing.

▲ On a sheet of hardboard, build up the shape that you want to create to make a mould for your mask. You can use a wide range of materials for this including Plasticine, pieces of plastic, cardboard. You can achieve a basic mask shape by using a plastic mask, and adding an additional feature with Plasticine, such as a bigger nose or a beard. It is not too important that the mould looks particularly neat, for example, you could use cardboard to provide a feature and this could be stuck onto the base with masking tape.

▲ When you make a mask, the mould has to come out easily, so the surface should be covered with a thin layer of Vaseline. (If you are making a solid model, then chicken wire is a useful way to give the overall shape.)

▲ Cut the Mod Roc up into small squares. Dip each one in tepid water for about three seconds, and cover over your mould with it. Make sure you cover the whole surface. Smooth the surface as you go, and use your fingers to add fine details. You can either leave holes for eyes and mouth or cut them out later when the Mod Roc has dried. When perfectly dry, remove the mould. Use the glass-paper to tidy up the edges. It can now be decorated, painted and varnished as required.

cut squares of materials

water

**DESIGN AND TECHNOLOGY**

**Food hygiene (see page 58)**

# Food safety and hygiene

▲ Long hair must be tied back.

▲ Clean aprons should be worn to protect your clothes and stop harmful bacteria on your clothes reaching the food.

▲ Cuts on hands should be covered with clean, blue waterproof dressings to stop harmful bacteria in the wound getting to the food and to make them easy to see in case they fall off.

▲ Wash hands with soap and clean, warm water to stop dirt and harmful bacteria on your hands reaching the food, and dry them with a clean dry towel so that you are not wiping harmful bacteria back onto your hands.

▲ Keep your hands clean.

▲ Do not cough or sneeze harmful bacteria all over the food, and do not pick at food or lick utensils, as harmful bacteria from your mouth will go into the food from your fingers, the knife, spoon or fork.

▲ Equipment should be kept clean at all times and should be used only for food preparation.

▲ Equipment should be dried with a clean, dry tea towel so that no harmful bacteria are spread, and disposable dish cloths cut up into small sections should be used so that any harmful substances get thrown away completely.

▲ Food preparation areas should be covered with clean plastic sheeting which is only used for food work, and this should be cleaned with an anti-bacterial cleaner.

**DESIGN AND TECHNOLOGY**

**Evaluating ready-made soup (see page 59)**

# Product evaluation questionnaire

Name _____ Date _____

Type of product _____ Tester   Male/Female      Age _____

Please look at the product.

I like it very much       I quite like it       It is OK       I dislike it quite a lot       I dislike it a lot

Now smell the product. What did you think?

I like it very much       I quite like it       It is OK       I dislike it quite a lot       I dislike it a lot

What do you think about the flavour of the product?

I like it very much       I quite like it       It is OK       I dislike it quite a lot       I dislike it a lot

What do you think about the texture of the product?

I like it very much       I quite like it       It is OK       I dislike it quite a lot       I dislike it a lot

What do you think of the product overall?

I like it very much       I quite like it       It is OK       I dislike it quite a lot       I dislike it a lot

✂ - - - - - - - - - - - - - - - - - - - - - - - - - - - - - - - - - - - - - - - - -

# Product analysis sheet

Name _____ Date _____

▲ Look at each food sample. Consider each of the following features of the food. Give a score between 1 and 9 in each section of the table. (1 represents VERY BAD and 9 represents VERY GOOD). Then add up the totals in each column to give a comparison.

| | Product W | Product N | Product R |
|---|---|---|---|
| Colour | | | |
| Smell | | | |
| Taste | | | |
| Thickness | | | |
| Texture | | | |
| Creaminess | | | |
| Overall appearance | | | |
| TOTALS | | | |

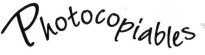

**Making butter (see page 63)**

# Making butter from cream

**1** Measure 150 ml of cream on the scales.

**2** Pour cream into a cooled jar.

**3** Screw the lid on tightly. Shake the jar until the cream begins to separate.

**4** Unscrew the lid and pour off the liquid – this is called *buttermilk*.

**5** Add a tablespoon of cold water to the jar.

**6** Mix the butter and water together using a fork.

**7** Take the butter out of the jar and make it into a neat shape. Add a little salt if you want to.

**8** Wrap the butter in some aluminium foil and put it into a refrigerator.

**9** Now try your home-made butter on some toast!

**DESIGN AND TECHNOLOGY**

**Fabrics (see page 68)**

## Investigating fabrics

Name _____     Date _____

▲ Using the information you discovered at home about five fabrics,
fill in this table.

| What can fabrics feel like? | What can fabrics look like? | Other things about fabrics |
|---|---|---|
| furry | dark | waterproof |
| smooth | patterned | flameproof |
| cold to touch | pastel | dry clean only |
| | | |
| | | |
| | | |
| | | |
| | | |
| | | |
| | | |

DESIGN AND
TECHNOLOGY

**A bookmark (see page 70)**

# Stitches and bookmark design

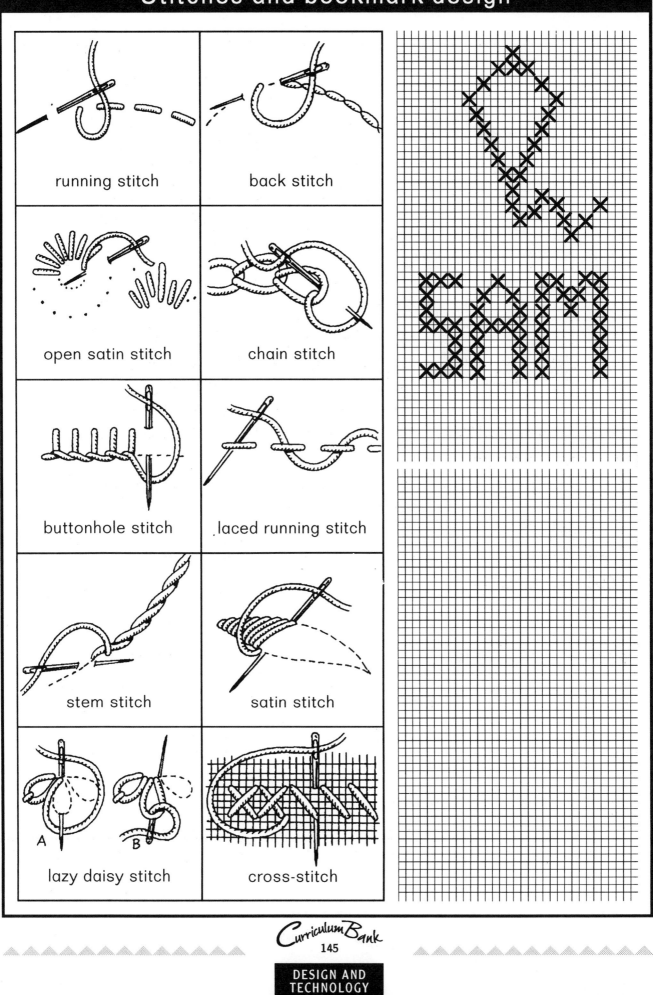

running stitch

back stitch

open satin stitch

chain stitch

buttonhole stitch

laced running stitch

stem stitch

satin stitch

lazy daisy stitch

cross-stitch

**DESIGN AND TECHNOLOGY**

**A tie-dyed bag (see page 71)**

# The process of tie-dying

▲ Put on your protective overall and plastic gloves.

▲ Take your piece of material, roll it up and then tie some knots in it.

▲ Put the fabric into the dye solution and stir it for ten minutes.

▲ Leave for another ten minutes.

▲ Rinse the fabric in water with a little drop of washing-up liquid.

▲ Put it under the cold water tap to rinse.

▲ Untie the knots, and iron it flat while it is still damp.

▲ You can experiment with other patterns by tying the material in different ways.

**A batik place mat (see page 72)**

# The process of batik

**1** Draw your design on paper and when you are happy with it go over it in black felt-tipped pen.

**2** Put your white fabric over the top of your design and clip the paper to it.

**3** Decide which parts of your design you wish to remain white and carefully cover these parts with melted wax.

**4** When the wax is cool add the fabric to your first chosen colour dye. You must use the lightest colour first. Then let the fabric dry.

**5** Decide which parts of the design are going to stay this colour. Cover these with more hot wax. Put the fabric into dye of the second colour. Again let the fabric dry. Repeat this process until your design is complete.

**6** Now you can remove the wax by putting the fabric between sheets of newspaper and using a hot iron. Put a sheet of plain paper between the fabric and the newspaper to stop ink stains spoiling your work. Keep changing the newspaper and plain paper until all the wax has disappeared.

**Glove puppet (see page 74)**

# Making a glove puppet

▲ Draw round your hand on a piece of paper.

▲ Now draw a basic glove puppet shape around your hand outline.

▲ Make any changes you want to at this stage. Draw another line about 1cm from outside your first outline. When you sew round the edge of the material you cannot sew right at the very edge – you need to sew about 1cm in. (This is called the seam allowance.)

▲ Cut your pattern out, and draw round it onto two sheets of paper. Keep your pattern safe.

▲ Now join the two paper cut-outs together using staples around the edge.

▲ Put it carefully on your hand. Is it the right size? Roughly draw some features and clothes onto the mock-up.

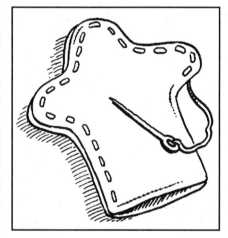

▲ Go on to make your glove puppet out of fabric.

▲ Use your pattern to make two copies in paper. Pin the patterns onto the fabric.

▲ Cut out the two pieces of fabric. Take the patterns off, and pin the two pieces together.

▲ Sew all the way round about 1cm from the edge of the puppet *except the bottom edge where you will need to put your hand!*

▲ Cut little nicks into the seam allowance, *but no further*, on all the curves.

▲ Turn the puppet inside out and ask your teacher to press it with an iron.

▲ Now, using fabric paints and things like beads, buttons and wool, decorate your glove puppet so that it looks like your chosen character.

**DESIGN AND TECHNOLOGY**

**Hairy hedgehog (see page 75)**

# Pattern for a hedgehog

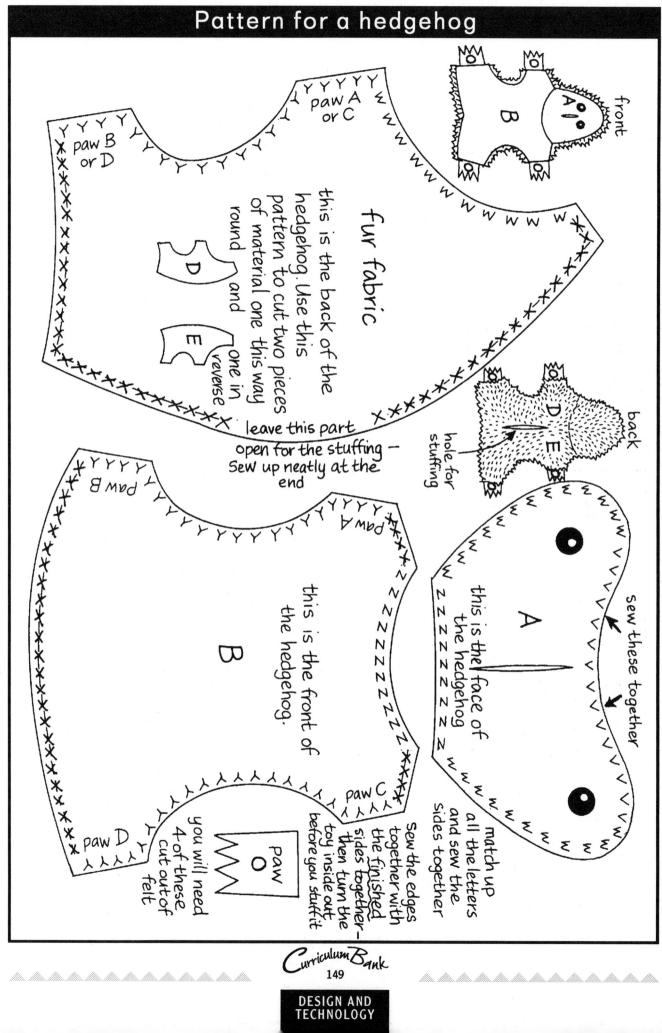

front

paw A or C

paw B or D

fur fabric

this is the back of the hedgehog. Use this pattern to cut two pieces of material one this way round and one in reverse

D

E

leave this part open for the stuffing — Sew up neatly at the end

back

D

E

hole for stuffing

this is the front of the hedgehog.

B

paw B

paw A

paw C

paw D

Paw O

you will need 4 of these cut out of felt

this is the face of the hedgehog

A

sew these together

match up all the letters and sew the sides together

sew the edges together with the finished sides together then turn the toy inside out before you stuff it

**DESIGN AND TECHNOLOGY**

**Evaluating torches (see page 78)**

## An exploded and annotated drawing of a torch

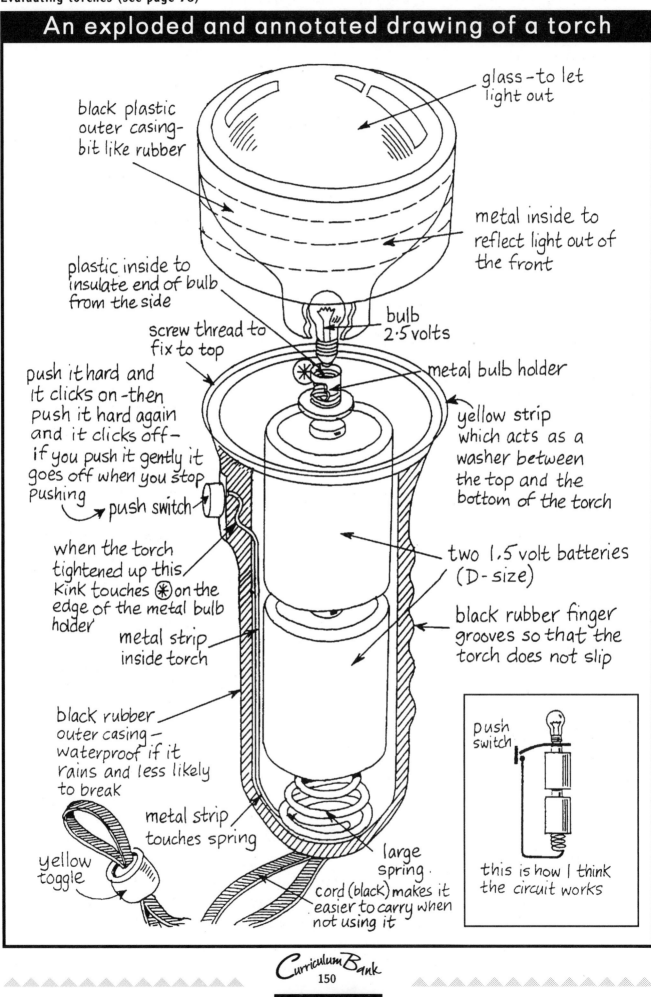

glass - to let light out

black plastic outer casing - bit like rubber

metal inside to reflect light out of the front

plastic inside to insulate end of bulb from the side

screw thread to fix to top

bulb 2·5 volts

metal bulb holder

push it hard and it clicks on - then push it hard again and it clicks off - if you push it gently it goes off when you stop pushing

push switch

yellow strip which acts as a washer between the top and the bottom of the torch

when the torch tightened up this kink touches ✳ on the edge of the metal bulb holder

metal strip inside torch

two 1.5 volt batteries (D-size)

black rubber finger grooves so that the torch does not slip

black rubber outer casing - waterproof if it rains and less likely to break

metal strip touches spring

yellow toggle

large spring.
cord (black) makes it easier to carry when not using it

push switch

this is how I think the circuit works

# Investigating switches

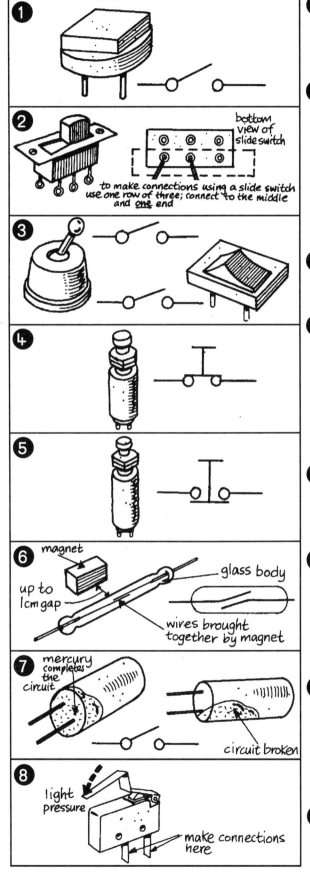

**1** A **push switch** – one push switches things on, the second push switches them off.

**2** A **slide switch** – pushed and pulled to switch on and off. They are cheap and light, so can be easily and neatly included in models. Because they often have a lot of connections at the back they can be used in complicated circuits, but are a little confusing in simple circuits.

**3** A **toggle or rocker switch** – flicked on or off like light switches.

**4** **Push-to-make switch** – when you push, the electricity flows through the circuit, but when you release it the switch goes off. This switch is no good for vehicles – you would need to run alongside keeping your finger pushed down all the time!

**5** **Push-to-break switch** – the electricity is normally flowing in the circuit. The circuit is broken when the switch is pushed.

**6** A **reed switch** – controlled by a magnet. When the magnet is near, the contacts are kept together and electricity can flow. These switches are often found in home burglar alarms.

**7** A **tilt switch** – contains a small drop of mercury (a metal liquid at room temperature). When the switch is tilted the drop can make contact with both connections and electricity can flow.

**8** A **microswitch** – only needs a very small pressure to switch it on – when it is released it is switched off.

DESIGN AND
TECHNOLOGY

# Making switches

▲ Use these drawings to help you make your own switches.

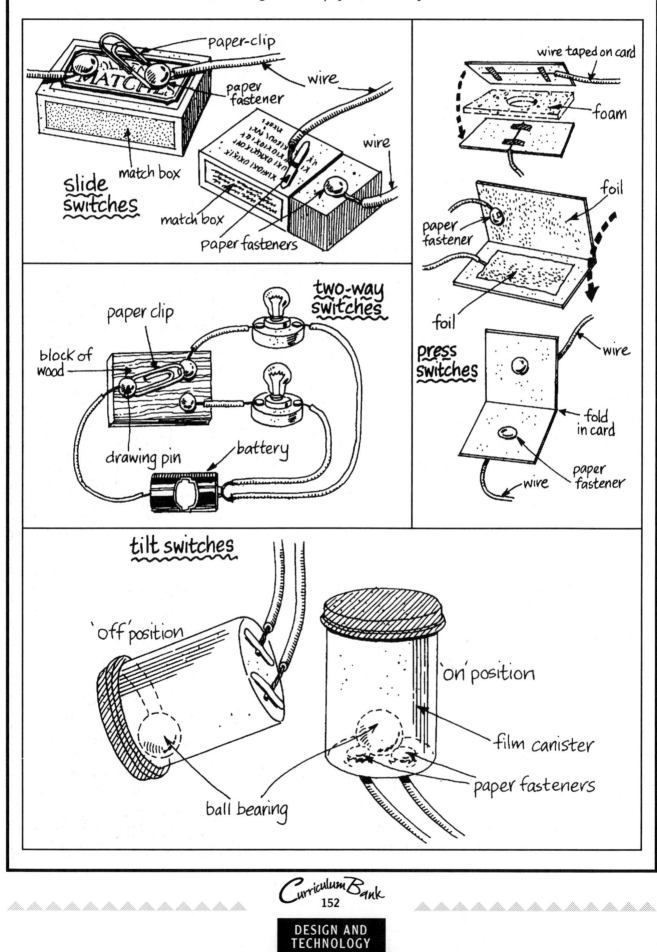

slide switches

paper-clip

wire

paper fastener

match box

match box

paper fasteners

wire

two-way switches

paper clip

block of wood

drawing pin

battery

wire taped on card

foam

foil

paper fastener

foil

press switches

wire

fold in card

paper fastener

wire

tilt switches

'off' position

'on' position

film canister

paper fasteners

ball bearing

**DESIGN AND TECHNOLOGY**

An entertaining display (see page 81)

# How to build your display

This sheet shows how you could include LEDs and a switch into the picture of a cat but you can choose your own picture.

▲ Stick the picture to a piece of foamboard using an adhesive.

▲ Use a paper drill to make two holes where the eyes of the cat are. Carefully push two green LEDs into the holes from behind, so that the green ends are showing as the eyes. Make a cardboard label with the cat's name on. Fold over the top edge to make a hinge and stick it on the cat's cushion. Make two small holes through the foamboard, behind the label. Put a brass paper fastener through one of them and a piece of multi-strand wire through the other. Splay out the multi-strand wire at the back of the label and stick a piece of aluminium foil over it. This is your *press switch*.

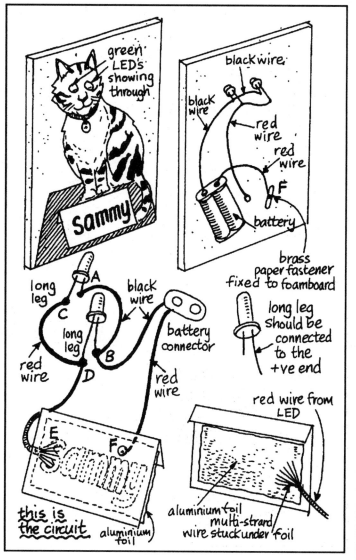

▲ Solder a wire from the short leg of one LED (A) to the short leg of the second LED (B). Solder the black wire of the battery clip to the short leg of the second LED (B). Solder a wire from the long leg of one LED (C) to the long leg of the second LED (D). Solder the free end of the piece of wire that is stuck under the aluminium foil (E) to the long leg of the second LED (D). Finally, solder the red wire of the battery clip to the back of the brass paper fastener (F). Attach a battery to the battery connector. When you press the cat's name her eyes light up. This is a *circuit diagram*. There are two LEDs connected in parallel, a home-made push switch, a battery, battery holder and battery connector.

DESIGN AND
TECHNOLOGY

**Making a membrane switch (see page 82)**

## A membrane switch

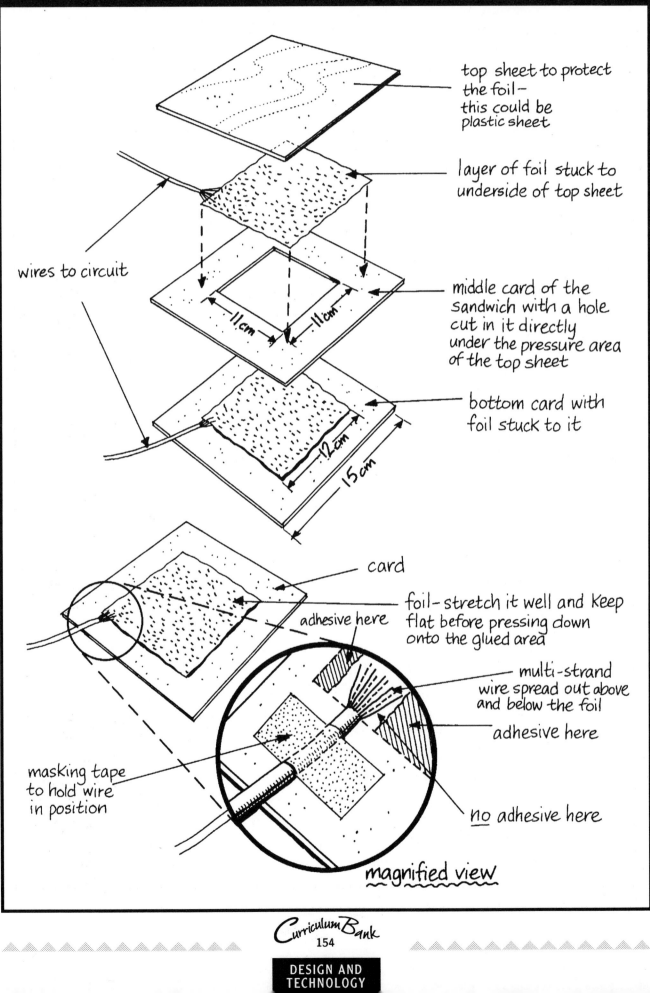

top sheet to protect the foil – this could be plastic sheet

layer of foil stuck to underside of top sheet

wires to circuit

11cm    11cm

middle card of the sandwich with a hole cut in it directly under the pressure area of the top sheet

bottom card with foil stuck to it

12cm

15cm

card

adhesive here

foil – stretch it well and keep flat before pressing down onto the glued area

multi-strand wire spread out above and below the foil

adhesive here

masking tape to hold wire in position

no adhesive here

magnified view

**DESIGN AND TECHNOLOGY**

**Making a membrane switch (see page 82)**

## Evaluative questions

Name _____ Date _____

Write here what you wanted your membrane switch to do.

Did it work every time someone came into the classroom? If it did not do you know what is wrong with it? How do you think you could make it work every time?

In a noisy classroom, could you always hear the buzzer? Would it be better if you used a much louder buzzer? What would be the disadvantages of a much louder buzzer?

Should the device be on all the time or should it just be used at particular times of day? Why?

Do you think the device will work for a long time? Will parts of it wear out? Which parts? How could you change the design so that it did not wear out so quickly?

Overall, do you think the device did what it was designed to do? Could you improve it in any way?

**Making a buggy (see page 86)**

## A simple motorised buggy

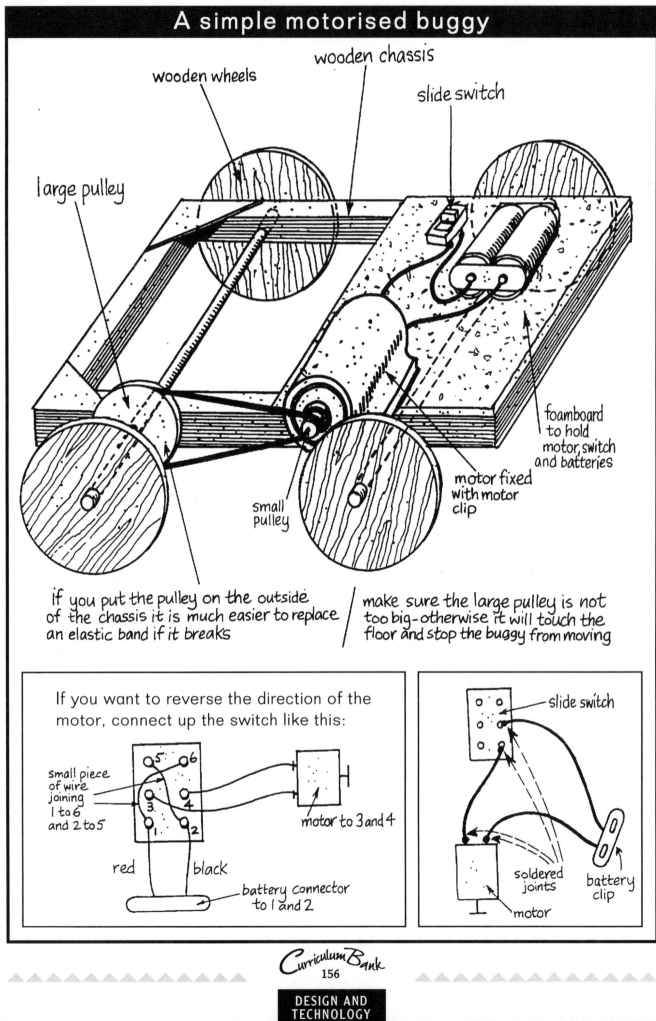

wooden wheels

wooden chassis

slide switch

large pulley

foamboard to hold motor, switch and batteries

motor fixed with motor clip

small pulley

if you put the pulley on the outside of the chassis it is much easier to replace an elastic band if it breaks

make sure the large pulley is not too big-otherwise it will touch the floor and stop the buggy from moving

If you want to reverse the direction of the motor, connect up the switch like this:

small piece of wire joining 1 to 6 and 2 to 5

5  6

3  4

1  2

motor to 3 and 4

red       black

battery connector to 1 and 2

slide switch

soldered joints

battery clip

motor

Interactive museum displays (see page 93)

## A membrane keypad

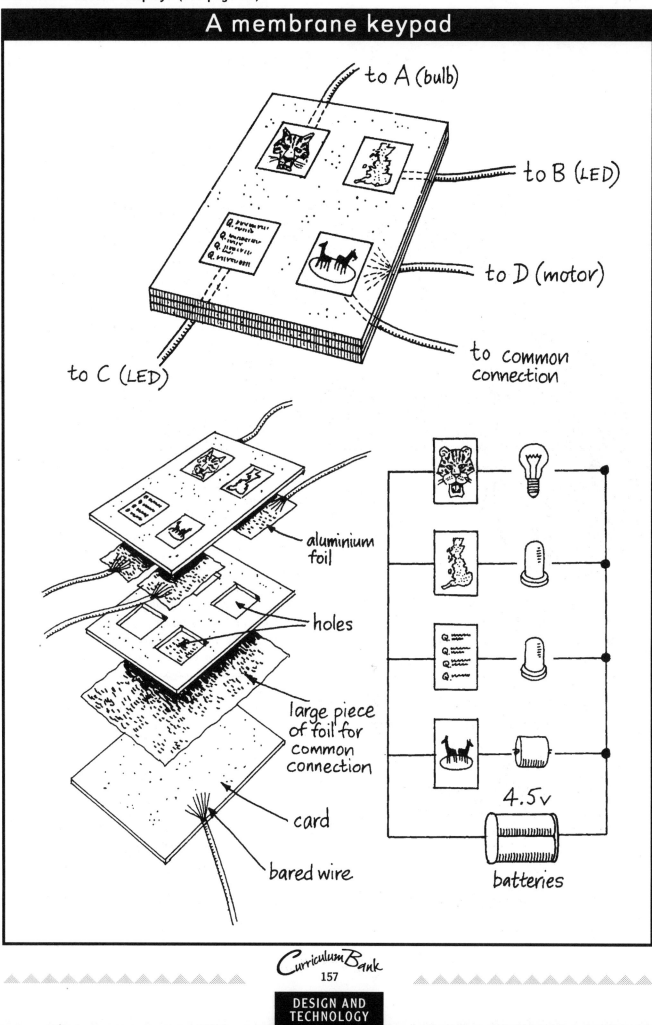

to A (bulb)

to B (LED)

to D (motor)

to common connection

to C (LED)

aluminium foil

holes

large piece of foil for common connection

card

bared wire

4.5v

batteries

# INFORMATION TECHNOLOGY WITHIN DESIGN AND TECHNOLOGY

The information technology opportunities outlined in this book can be used to develop and assess children's IT capability as outlined in the National Curriculum. Types of software rather than names of specific programs have been mentioned to enable teachers to use the ideas regardless of which computer they have access to. Teachers may still want to include specific software which runs on their computers and addresses the content and understanding of the design and technology being taught. They should be aware that although such software may assist pupils in their learning of design and technology, it may add little to their IT development.

## Main IT focus

Design and technology lends itself to a wide range of IT applications. Information is given in the area of graphics software and control which feature throughout the activities.

## Drawing and art packages

A number of simple art, graphics and computer-aided design packages are available for children across a wide range of computers. These tend to fall into two categories. The first comprises drawing or CAD packages which enable children to draw lines and shapes and add text. The lines and shapes can be manipulated, re-sized, moved, stretched and rotated. Colours can be changed and shapes filled. On more sophisticated packages the shapes can be combined to form a single 'object', for example, all the components of a puppet can be drawn separately, combined and then kept as a puppet. Text can be added and in some packages, fonts, sizes and colours changed. In order to help children line up the shapes and lines as they draw them, it is usually possible to have a background grid. When the 'snap to grid' option is turned on, the ends of the drawn lines are automatically joined to the nearest point on the grid. Computer-aided design packages use similar facilities but the tools are closely aligned to a two-dimensional drafting process. Some software like SPEX enables children to design in two-dimensional and then to look at their design as a three-dimensional object.

The second category of packages is an art or painting one which use a different approach, but can often achieve the same results. The drawing process is more akin to using a pencil or brush. Lines and shapes are drawn by colouring in the individual *pixels* of the screen. Very detailed work and effects can be produced to create pictures which mirror the results of paint on paper. Such packages usually have a range of tools such as brushes, sprays and rollers for adding and creating different effects. Text can be added, coloured and re-sized. Scanned images made using a hand scanner can be combined in such packages and edited, by changing colours or masking out parts of the picture.

The skills that children need to be taught are similar to word processing, but related to pictures. They need to:
▲ select appropriate drawing tools;
▲ change features such as line thickness;
▲ copy or duplicate shapes;
▲ zoom into parts of the drawing to make fine details;
▲ edit and erase shapes and lines;
▲ move, re-size and rotate shapes and lines;
▲ create 'objects' by combining parts of a drawing together;
▲ save and retrieve the full picture or a part of it;
▲ select and add or create new colours;
▲ add, re-size and colour text;
▲ link text to make an annotated drawing;
▲ save and retrieve their work from a disk;
▲ set up the printer and print out their work.

## Using control

Design and technology provides children with many opportunities to explore and develop skills in the use of computer control. In order for children to tackle this kind of work three sorts of equipment are needed.

The first is a range of controllable objects. These consist of lights, buzzers, bells and motors. All are worked electrically from batteries and to get started, children need to know how to make a simple circuit and control it using a switch. When they start to use these devices within a model, it is a good idea to use construction kits such as technical LEGO which allow models to be built easily and quickly.

The electrical circuits or models then need to be connected to the computer. This is achieved through an interface (the second sort of equipment needed) which may be called a 'buffer' or 'control' box. This is connected to the serial or analogue port of the computer; you will need an appropriate box and cables which match the computer to be used. The box has two functions. Firstly, it protects the computer from the voltages of the electrical circuits as they may be using a voltage much larger than the computer's internal circuitry. Secondly, it provides a link to the computer which will turn on and off the various components which are connected to the box. Most simple control boxes have sockets for three or four 'outputs' (lights, motors, buzzers). The boxes will also have 'input' sockets which are used to connect sensors.

The third sort of equipment is software to actually control the devices connected to the control box. Early software tended to use a LOGO type programming language which was text based, often like the commands used for controlling a floor turtle. The commands are simple and encourage children to think in logical steps and to write well-structured programs. Recent software which uses a graphical interface (Windows or RISCOS) has made it easier for children to program the actions through the use of pictures or menus.

Throughout this type of work it is important that children begin to recognise and understand how much of the world around them is using forms of computer sensing and control.

The grids below relate the activities in this book to specific areas of IT and to relevant software resources. Activities are referenced by page number. (Bold page numbers indicate activities which have an expanded IT content.) The software listed in the second grid is a selection of programs generally available to primary schools, and is not intended as a recommended list. The software featured should be available from most good educational software retailers.

| AREA OF IT | TYPE OF SOFTWARE | ACTIVITIES (PAGE NOS.) | | | | | | | | |
|---|---|---|---|---|---|---|---|---|---|---|
| | | CHP 1 | CHP 2 | CHP 3 | CHP 4 | CHP 5 | CHP 6 | CHP 7 | CHP 8 | CHP 9 |
| Communicating Info | Word Processor | 18 | 24, 30, 31 | 38, 40, 41, 42, 44, 45 | 48, 52, 54 | 58, 64 | | | | All |
| Communicating Info | DTP | 18 | 24 | 45 | 54 | 58, 61 | | 86 | | 100, 101, 102 |
| Communicating Info | Drawing package | 14, 15, 17 | 25, 27 | 36, 40 | 49 | 61, 63, 65 | 68, 70 | 78, 81, 86 | | 96, 98, 99, 100, 102, 103 |
| Communicating Info | Art package | | 27 | | 49 | 63, 65 | | | | 96, 98, 99, 100, 101, 102 |
| Communicating Info | CAD package | | 25 | 40, 42 | | | | 78, 81, 86 | | 96, 98, 99, 102, 103 |
| Communicating Info | Framework | 14, 20 | 25 | | | | | | | |
| Communicating Info | Multi-media | | | 38, 41 | 48, 52 | 61 | | | | |
| Communicating Info | Animation software | | 31 | | | | | | | |
| Information Handling | Graphing software | | | | 55 | | | | | 100 |
| Information Handling | Database | | | 36 | | 59 | 68 | | | 100 |
| Information Handling | Spreadsheet | | | 37, 45 | | 59 | | | | |
| Information Handling | Branching database | | | | | | 68 | | | |
| Information Handling | CD-ROM | 17, 20 | 24, 30, 31 | 38, 41 | 52, 55 | | | | | |
| Control | Control | | | 45 | | | | 81, 82 | 90, 93 | 101 |

| SOFTWARE TYPE | BBC/MASTER | RISCOS | NIMBUS/186 | WINDOWS | MACINTOSH |
|---|---|---|---|---|---|
| Word Processor | Pendown Folio | Pendown Desk Top Folio | All Write Write On | Word for Windows Kid Works 2 Creative Writer | Kid Works 2 Easy Works Creative Writer |
| DTP | Front Page Extra Typsetter | Desk Top Folio Pendown DTP Bearword | Front Page Extra NewSPAper | Creative Writer NewSPAper | Creative Writer |
| Framework | | My World 2 | | My World 2 | |
| Drawing Package | | Draw Picture IT | PaintSpa | Claris Works | Claris Works |
| Art Package | Image | 1st Paint Kid Pix, Splash | NewSPAint | Colour Magic Kid Pix 2, Fine Artist | Kid Pix 2, Fine Artist Flying Colours |
| CAD package | | CADet | FlexiCad | Kid Cad FlexiCad, BoxIT | |
| Multi-media Authoring | | Magpie Hyperstudio Genesis | | Genesis Hyperstudio Illuminatus | Hyperstudio |
| Branching Database | Bramch | ReTreeval, Tree | Branch | ReTreeval, Tree | |
| Database | Grass | Junior Pinpoint Find IT KeyNote | Grass | Sparks Claris Works Information Workshop | Claris Works Easy Works |
| CD ROM | | Children's Micropedia Hutchinsons | | Encarta 96 Children's Micropedia Grolier | Encarta 96 Grolier |
| Graphing Software | Datashow | Pictogram Picture Point DataSweet | Datagraph | Datagraph Easy Works | Easy Works |
| Spreadsheet | Grasshopper Pigeonhole | Grasshopper Advantage Key Count | Grasshopper | Excel starting Grid Claris Works Sparks | Claris Works |
| Control | Contact | Contact Control IT CoCo | Contact | Contact | MacContact |

DESIGN AND TECHNOLOGY

| | ENGLISH | MATHEMATICS | SCIENCE | HISTORY | GEOGRAPHY | IT | ART | MUSIC | RE | PE |
|---|---|---|---|---|---|---|---|---|---|---|
| **STRUCTURES** | Instructions on how to make products. Letters about ideas for a playground. | Research and design of nets. Investigating 3-D structures. | Stability of structures and strength. Investigating forces. | Identifying building materials and use throughout history; construction techniques. | Structures in other countries eg. Eiffel Tower. | CAD programs to design own packaging. Using a drawing program. | Techniques for decorating the packing or the geodesic building. | Structural features of musical instruments. | The nature of buildings used for worship within different religions. | Existing play equipment to construct new obstacle courses. |
| **MECHANISMS** | Producing advertising copy for products made. | Understanding of simple ratios for pulleys and gears. | Scientific principles of levers, pulleys and gears. | Victorian toys which make use of optical illusions. | Mechanisms in the environment related to transport. | Use of clip art in their models. Using a drawing program. | Creating illustrations for the zoetrope. | Music that is appropriate for silent movies. | | Use of mechanisms in gym equipment. |
| **ENERGY** | Writing a script for their presentation. | The amount of energy obtained from a range of devices and which are most expensive to run. | Scientific concepts of energy conservation. Different sources of energy. | Amount of energy used by previous generations. A comparison of domestic and industrial use. | Creating and annotating a plan of the school. Sources of energy in the world. | Creating visual material for their presentation. Creating symbols for plans. | Selecting music suitable as backgroud for a display . | Sound energy. The size of instruments; the amount of energy required to play them. | | Looking at energy use in physical activities. |
| **MOULDABLE MATERIALS** | Advertising copy for the craft fair products. | | How materials change both permanently and temporarily when processed. | Crafts which have been practised in other times. | Artefacts which are produced in other countries. Masks in other countries. | Using CD-ROM for research into different types of materials. | Decorating clay pots. Using skills developed in art to decorate products. | Looking at percussion instruments. | Jewellery, masks, clay and salt dough products with a religious theme. | Possible sports injuries – how they could be avoided. |
| **FOOD** | Writing food labels. Producing advertising for food products. | Accurate weighing and measuring of ingredients. Questionnaire. | Food safety procedures. Change related to mixing, heating. | Recipes from history and features such as expense and healthiness. | Food ingredients from other countries. | | Designing advertising materials and packaging. | Choosing or writing music for their advertisements. | | |
| **TEXTILES** | Stories about a soft toy they have made for a young child. | The production of accurate templates and patterns. | Mixtures, strength and other properties of fabrics. Fair tests. | Fabric design from other generations. | Textile decorating techniques from other countries. | Design and CAD programs to create patterns. Use of sewing machine. | Decorating textiles. | | Appropriate religious pictures for a bookmark. | |
| **ELECTRICITY** | Summarise details of an investigation into the annotations of a diagram. | Accurate measuring when constructing the membrane switch. | Electrical circuits: series and parallel, switches, bulbs, LEDs, voltage. | Amount of electricity used by previous generations. | Electrical use in other countries. | Making use of clip art in models. Using a drawing program to create designs. | Creating a drawing which includes LEDs and a switch. | Electrical and acoustic instruments – advantages/ disadvantages. | Using up the Earth's resources for the production of electricity. | |
| **CONTROL** | Writing the information needed for the museum display. | Programming skills using LOGO or similar devices. | Series and parallel circuits, two-way switches. | Looking at what happened on the roads before traffic lights. | The placing of traffic lights and what they do to traffic flow. | Creating illustrations for part of the museum display. | Producing illustrations using computer software. | | Using a religious theme for the museum display. | |
| **DMA** | Producing a play which can be performed by the puppets. | Accurate measuring and production of patterns. | Series and parallel circuits, two-way switches. | Existing and earlier products to inform designing and making. | Clothes and footwear from other cultures. | Controlling the fairground ride using a computer. | Appropriate techniques to decorate and finish products. | Choosing or writing music suitable for a fairground ride. | Puppet play could have a religious theme. | How their body moves to design string puppets. |